WORKBOOK

FOR

PISTON/DEVOTO

HARMONY

FOURTH EDITION

BY

ARTHUR JANNERY

RADFORD COLLEGE

W · W · NORTON & COMPANY

NEW YORK   LONDON

Copyright © 1979 by W. W. Norton & Company, Inc.

Published simultaneously in Canada by George J. McLeod Limited,

Toronto. Printed in the United States of America.

ISBN 0 393 95071 9

1 2 3 4 5 6 7 8 9 0

Contents

Foreword

This Workbook is designed to accompany Piston's *Harmony*, Fourth Edition, and to supplement it where necessary. Because most students will have had previous training in written theory, and some a good deal of it, "where necessary" takes in a lot of territory. Some of you will welcome the persistent drill of fundamentals that this Workbook supplies; many will profit from the systematic reviews; still others may spend more time on the composition exercises offered.

Given the wide differences in musical background of beginning harmony students today, it was felt that a separate volume of exercises would be the best place to accommodate individual needs. The necessary flexibility could not have been incorporated into the main text without making it much larger than it already is.

The basic organization of this Workbook is straightforward. Each unit is matched to the corresponding chapter in the main text. Within each unit there are usually five sections, although not all five were considered necessary for all units. The categories are:

A. A list of *Words to Know*, define, memorize, compare, or contrast. Definitions of all of these will be found in the corresponding chapter of the main text, or may be looked up in the Index.

B. *Technical Exercises*. For the most part these are drill exercises, a sort of mental calisthenics, requiring many short, definite, and prompt answers. The trick is to learn to do them by concentrated effort, with enough speed and accuracy so that they don't become boring.

C. *Programmed Series; Analysis*. In the earlier units these analytical exercises will help you develop some reduction techniques, which are not much talked about in the main text but which you will find very valuable in your harmonic analysis of music. In the first few units these exercises are called "Programmed Series" because they are laid out systematically in a frame-by-frame format. The Section C exercises of the later units only occasionally call for reductions and are less formal; they are simply designated "Analysis."

D. *Composition Activities*. These form such a special category that perhaps they shouldn't be called "exercises." Rather, they are intended to appeal to your creative instincts. Those of you who have already composed music will have no difficulty responding to the suggestions given. On the other hand, many of you may never have tried to compose before, and it is to the hesitant beginners that these Composition Activities are especially addressed. It is important to remember that the Composition Activities are unlike the other exercises in that you must treat them much more freely. Certainly you should try to comply precisely with the given conditions, and you should apply the rules you have learned; but at the same time you should always try to make interesting music, even when this means including things not mentioned in the directions. In these efforts, as in all original work, the honest opinions of your teacher, and of your fellow students, will be valuable.

E. *Self Tests*. These are brief verbal summaries that will be useful for memorization and spot checking of information.

Exercises are not provided in this Workbook to accompany Part II of the main text, just as they were not provided there. However, it should not be difficult to use the chapters of Part II as the basis for compositional exercises. Part II is not covered here chiefly because it was felt that this Workbook will find its greatest usefulness in the earlier stages of harmony study. This book is, after all, a Workbook rather than a textbook or reference book; it is designed to enable you to work directly and abundantly with the material, to get your hands dirty with notes, so to speak. The kind of experience you will acquire here may be only a beginning, but a beginning that is more than just ear training or memorization of rules: it involves the things composers think about. And that, in turn, is an access to music that will serve you well both as performer and listener.

Acknowledgments

I wish to thank the many students who have been in my music theory sequence over the past twelve years; the insight they have provided has been critical in the preparation of this *Workbook*.

Maurice Hinson of Southern Baptist Theological Seminary in Louisville made available his editions of *Piano Music in Nineteenth-Century America,* which were most helpful in the selection of musical examples. The review of the final manuscript and the subsequent suggestions by Leo Kraft of Queens College of the City University of New York were also important.

The staff of W. W. Norton & Company deserves much praise, as does Claire Brook, Music Editor, for the direction that she helped to achieve in the initial stages, as well as for her many supportive activities during the entire project.

My wife Marti is acknowledged for the support that she has always provided.

Finally, I am very much in debt to Mark DeVoto; for his excellent work that is now manifest in the Piston/DeVoto *Harmony*; for his contribution of original exercises for Units 10 and 18; and for his painstaking editorial work during all phases of the preparation of this *Workbook*. The accuracy and relevancy of many of the musical examples, as well as the correlation of materials and style of the *Workbook* with its parent text benefited immeasurably through his efforts.

Arthur Jannery
Radford, Virginia
May 1979

Scales and Intervals

SECTION A

Words to Know

Define and memorize:

scale	harmonic inversion	octave	circle of fifths
keynote	pitch	tonic	tonal music
subdominant	supertonic	dominant	mediant
subtonic	submediant	interval	leading-tone
minor	perfect	augmented	major
melodic interval	diminished	harmonic interval	enharmonic intervals
compound interval	half step	unison	whole step

Contrast:

chromatic/diatonic
consonant/dissonant
tone/note

SECTION B

Technical Exercises

1. Add tones that will form half steps *below* and *above* each given tone, as in the Example.

2. Using appropriate accidental signs (sharps for ascending motion, and flats for descending motion), and without altering the initial pitch of each example, transform each of the following into chromatic lines.

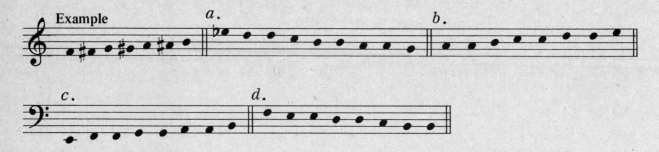

3. Fill in the notes necessary to create ascending and descending chromatic scales between the given pitches as indicated. (Remember that as a rule sharps are used when the scale ascends, and flats when it descends.)

4. Examine the descending and ascending scale lines respectively in the two excerpts that follow. Is either of these lines a chromatic scale? Are both? In the second excerpt, why is there no sharp sign placed before the F's and C's?

_____

_____

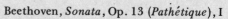

Beethoven, *Sonata*, Op. 13 (*Pathétique*), I

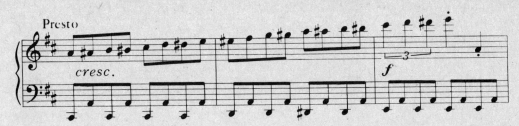

5. Add tones that will be both a whole step and a letter name above and below the given tone. (See the Example.)

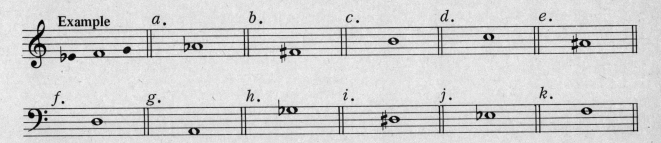

6. Identify each pair of tones as either a half step (¹/₂) or a whole step (1) apart.

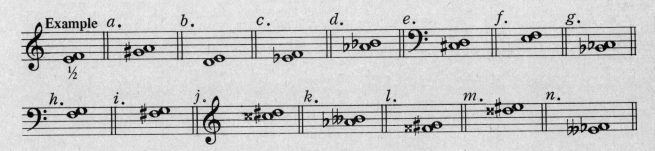

7. Write out the intervallic series of whole step, whole step, and half step (1–1–¹/₂), ascending, starting on each of the given tones. Label the intervals as shown in the Example.

8. Using each of the given tones either as a tonic or dominant note, write the three ascending major scale degrees that should follow.

Tonic is given:

Dominant is given:

9. In the following ascending and descending scale segments, mark each pair of tones that are a half step apart as shown in the Example. Determine the keynote of the major scale within each line and circle it.

Example

10. Circle each pair of tones that form a half step. Indicate whether or not each segment is a major scale.

Example

11. Recite the letter names of the sharps as they appear in key signatures from left to right, beginning with the one-sharp key signature and ending with seven sharps. Name the keynote of each respective major scale.

12. Repeat the procedure given in No. 11 above for major keys having signatures of one to seven flats. (You should return to these questions regularly and recite the signatures until they are second nature to you.)

13. Write the signatures for the following major keys:

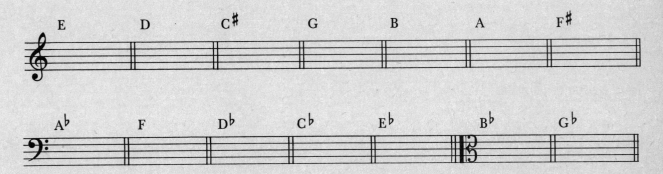

14. Indicate the names of the major keys that correspond to the following signatures:

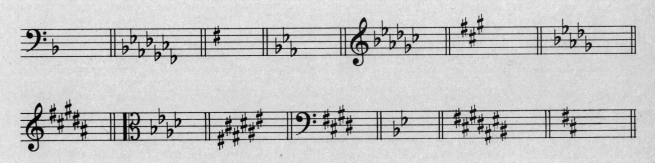

15. Give the general name for each of the following harmonic intervals:

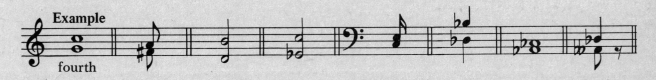

16. Give the general name for each of the following melodic intervals:

5

17. Fill in the space between the given interval with notes of the major scale whose key-note is the lower tone. Indicate whether or not the upper note is a degree of this scale.

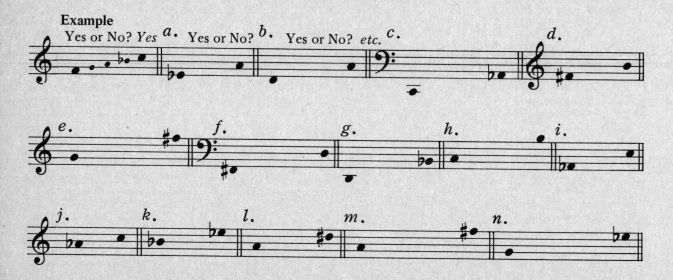

18. Give both the specific and general names for each of the following intervals:

19. Each of the following groups contains intervals of the same general type, but with different specific names. Give both the general and the specific names.

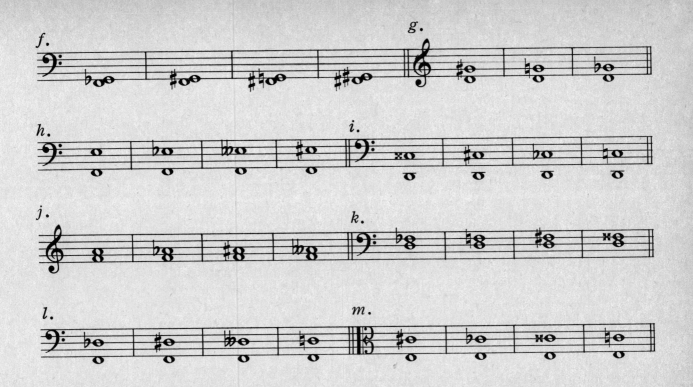

20. Give the general and specific names for each of the following harmonic intervals:

21. Give the general and specific names for each of the following melodic intervals:

22. Use the tone series given below for oral practice in constructing different intervals. (Don't write down the answers.) Proceed through each series, practicing with a particular interval above or below the given tones. When you feel that you can easily construct that interval, pick another one and repeat the procedure, until you have practiced every kind of interval from unison through octave, whether perfect, major, minor, augmented, or diminished.

The following order is suggested:

a. major seconds	m. augmented fifths
b. minor seconds	n. major sixths
c. augmented seconds	o. minor sixths
d. major thirds	p. diminished sixths
e. minor thirds	q. augmented sixths
f. diminished thirds	r. major sevenths
g. augmented thirds	s. minor sevenths
h. perfect fourths	t. diminished sevenths
i. diminished fourths	u. perfect octaves
j. augmented fourths	v. diminished octaves
k. perfect fifths	w. augmented octaves
l. diminished fifths	

23. Use the following excerpt for additional practice in identifying melodic and harmonic intervals. (It should be apparent that nearly any piece of music will provide good material for this sort of practice.)

Vivaldi, *Concerto Grosso*, Op. 3, No. 11, II (from *L'estro armonico*)

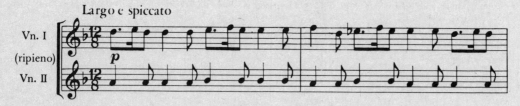

8

24. Given below are the rhythms and starting pitches for the opening phrases of five familiar tunes. The remaining pitches are partially indicated by the melodic interval labels appearing below each line. (A pitch may be either above or below the preceding tone; that is, whether the melodic interval indicated is up or down isn't specified!) Can you name each tune?

Programmed Series

1. Examine the melody given below. How many different pitches can you find in it? (Pitches which differ by a perfect octave are to be counted only once.)

Traditional melody, *Amazing Grace*

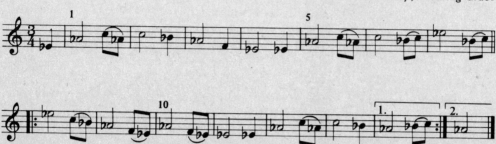

2. Notate below all of the different pitches you found above, in the order of their appearance.

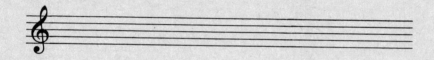

3. Observe that this melody keeps returning to a tone which is more or less in the middle of the range of the melody, and which is used more than any other single pitch. This pitch usually receives the first-beat accent and most often has a duration of at least a half note. Name the pitch.

4. It also may be observed that A flat is the first significant tone in this tune (the upbeat E flat is of lesser duration and is metrically weak). A flat is also the tone that is heard last, providing a feeling of ending, or finality, to the tune. Which two other tones in the melody seem also to have a special importance due to their relatively greater duration and metrical stress?

5. After playing or singing through *Amazing Grace* several times, and examing the answers to Questions 1—4 above, we may deduce that the melody is in the key of

_____ .

6. Examine the following melody, *100 Psalm Tune* (also known as *Old Hundredth*) from the *Genevan Psalter* of 1551 (text from the *Bay Psalm Book*, Boston, 1698):

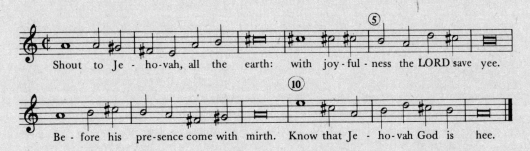

7. List the different pitches of the tune above, in the order of their appearance.

8. Deduce a key signature for *100 Psalm Tune* from the collection of pitches you have just assembled above. Write the key signature on the staff below.

9. The key signature, along with the pitches stressed at the beginning and end of the hymn, indicate that *100 Psalm Tune* is in the key of _____ .

10. Examine the following passage taken from Bach's *Two-Part Invention* No. 8:

11. The excerpt above has an entire scale suggested within its first two measures. On the staff below, write the different pitches of the melody in their order of appearance. (As before, octave-equivalent pitches may be counted only once.)

12. Arrange the tones above in scalar order, with the half steps between the third and fourth degrees and the seventh and eighth. (The eighth degree, equivalent to the first degree, was ruled out by the requirements of No. 11 above, and must now be put back in.)

13. We should now probably deduce that the beginning of the Bach melody is in the key of _____ .

14. The scale we have just written down in No. 12 above does not, however, remain the source of all the pitches in the entire Bach melody quoted above. Beginning at measure 5 there is a change. The final measures of the excerpt place particular stress on _____ .

15. On the staff below, write the pitches of the last four measures of the excerpt, in order of their appearance.

16. Rearrange these pitches (you will need to use the octave equivalents of some of them) so that they form a major scale. What is the keynote of this scale? By implication, in what key is the end of the excerpt? What else in the passage might lead us to make that inference?

17. What scale serves as the basis of the following excerpt?

Kuhlau, *Sonatina*, Op. 20, No. 1, I

18. The following melody begins on D. What key is it in?

Couperin, *Harpsichord Pieces, Book III*: Eighteenth Order, *Soeur Monique*

19. In the following example, note carefully the emphasis on the pitch G. In what key is this melody? Is the key in any way ambiguous?

Mendelssohn, *Songs without Words*, Op. 102: No. 3, *Tarantella*

20. The fragment that follows is in what key?

Composition Activities

In all your Composition Activities, you should make every effort to think of your work specifically in terms of how it might be performed in your classes and laboratory meetings. To this end you should try to learn how different instruments and voices sound in their different ranges and combinations, and what they can do best. Such things are covered in detail in an orchestration course, but you will find it very advantageous to acquire an elementary knowledge of instruments and voices as you work on the Composition Activities here.

In the earliest units of this Workbook, we have provided blank staves for writing out your compositions. As the assignments become longer and more complicated, you will find a music notebook with ten or twelve staves per page indispensable for sketching out your original pieces.

The list of ranges and the transposition charts given in the Appendices will serve as a convenient beginning, and an important one. But most important of all is listening to the actual sound of instruments and voices often enough and carefully enough to become firmly familiar with their individualities. That way you will learn both their technical possibilities and their musical suitabilities, as well as what they cannot do or what they ought not to be asked to do. In these activities, the best way to learn is actually to try out what you write, or have it tried out for you. Then you will discover, for instance, that a lot of fast notes over a wide range played brilliantly on a cello will probably sound poorly when attempted by a trombone; on the other hand, an ordinary chordal passage for strings might gain much when played by a brass ensemble.

A question often asked of professional composers is whether or not it is advisable to compose at the piano. Today as well as in the past, the answer is that some composers do and some do not. Certainly the piano can be a great help at any stage in the compositional process; but it should not become an aural crutch. You may find that you need the piano more at first than later on, and that eventually you can get along without it most of the time; this is a good goal to strive for in your study of harmony. If you become a serious composer, you will be beyond needing advice of this kind. But let us repeat: try out what you write, not just so that you will know whether it is correct, but so that it will be live music.

1. Compose a stately melody for a solo brass instrument, based on the appropriate three-note fragment given below:

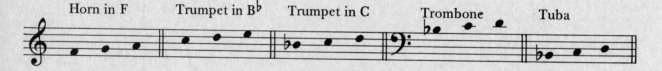

(You may use additional octave equivalents of any of the three given pitches, provided they are in the instrument's practical range.*) Write your piece in 4/4 meter, *Andante maestoso*, and limit it to approximately eight to twelve measures. Be certain to indicate all dynamics, phrasing, and articulation, by means of appropriate markings.

---

*See Appendix II.

2. Write a rhythmic pattern (8 measures, to be repeated a number of times) for snare drum that will go well with the bass drum part given below. Write several possibilities and try them out. Select the one you like best and improve upon it. Repeat the whole process, until you have three or four different parts that you could use with the given bass drum beat.

Snare drum ($\quad$ =90)

Bass drum

a.

S. D.

b.

S. D.

c.

S. D.

3. Write a fast melody, gay or even boisterous, for clarinet or bassoon. Make it exactly eight measures long, 2/4 time, *Allegro ma non troppo*. Use the scale fragment given below, with octave equivalents within the instrument's range if you wish. Indicate dynamics, phrasing, and articulation carefully.

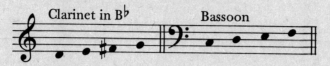

4. Write a soft lyric melody, *Andante cantabile*, 6/8 time, for muted cello, based entirely upon the following:

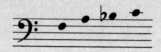

5. Compose a melody in F major for the following text, using the rhythm and meter given:

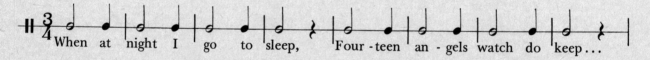

This will not be a complete composition; create a feeling of wanting to go on at the end. Choose a suitable tempo and dynamics.

6. Now write another setting of the text above, using the same rhythm and meter but otherwise completely different. Use the key of D major; choose your own dynamics and tempo.

7. For a final setting of the same text, you may choose your own rhythm, meter, tempo, and major key. You may also use two or more pitches for each syllable of the text, where you feel that such a treatment is appropriate. Do not exceed ten measures in length.

Self Test

1. The sound that is almost an exact duplicate of a given pitch, either twelve half steps or seven letter names higher or lower, is the _____ .

2. A diatonic scale will have _____ different tones.

3. The chromatic scale has _____ more constituent tones than does the diatonic scale.

4. The major scale has the following succession of whole and half steps: _____ _____ _____ _____ _____ _____ _____ .

5. Another name for "keynote" is _____ .

6. The names of the scale degrees are: I _____ , II _____ , III _____ , IV _____ , V _____ , VI _____ , and VII _____ .

7. Distances between pitches are called _____ .

8. The general names of intervals are determined by counting the _____ between constituent tones.

9. The specific names of intervals are found by noting the correspondence between the upper tone and the _____ scale of the lower tone.

10. If the two tones of an interval are successive, that is, they follow each other in time, the interval is called a _____ interval.

11. If the tones sound together it is called a _____ interval.

12. Thirds may be either _____ , _____ , _____ , or _____ .

13. Unisons, octaves, fourths, and fifths may be _____ , _____ , or _____ .

14. An interval larger than an octave is called a _____ interval.

15. An interval of an octave or less is called a _____ interval.

16. Those intervals which sound relatively stable are referred to as _____ intervals.

17. Those intervals whose sounds are relatively restless and in need of resolution to a stable interval are called _____ intervals.

18. The consonant intervals are the _____ , _____ , _____ , _____ , _____ , _____ , _____ , and sometimes the _____ .

19. The major and minor seconds and sevenths are _____ intervals.

20. Augmented and diminished intervals are considered to be _____ intervals.

21. A major interval becomes _____ when inverted.

22. An augmented interval becomes _____ when inverted.

23. The inversion of any perfect interval will be _____ .

24. A seventh when inverted becomes a _____ .

25. A major third inverts to become a _____ .

26. The following intervals:

are called _____ of each other.

27. The order of sharps in the key signature of seven sharps, read from left to right, is _____ , _____ , _____ , _____ , _____ , _____ , and _____ .

28. The order of flats in the key signature of seven flats, read from left to right, is _____ , _____ , _____ , _____ , _____ , _____ , and _____ .

29. The keynotes of the major keys in order from one sharp through seven sharps are _____ , _____ , _____ , _____ , _____ , _____ , and _____ .

30. The keynotes of the major keys in order from one flat through seven flats are _____ , _____ , _____ , _____ , _____ , _____ , and _____ .

Triads

SECTION A

Words to Know

Define and memorize:

root	minor triad	tenor	alto
third	diminished triad	range	augmented triad
fifth	I, II, III, IV, etc.	doubling	second inversion
root position	soprano	spacing	open position
first inversion	SATB	close position	chord factor
major triad	bass	four-part writing	

Contrast:

chord/triad
diminished/augmented

SECTION B

Technical Exercises

1. Add a note above each of the given tones that will create major thirds:

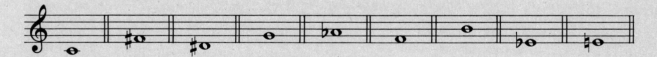

2. The answers to No. 1 are below. Add to these a perfect fifth above each lower tone; the perfect fifth and the major third together will form a major triad.

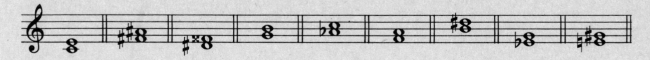

3. Add a major third and a perfect fifth above each given tone, forming major triads.

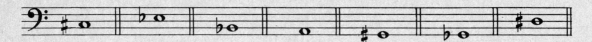

4. Lower the third of each of the given major triads, thus transforming them into minor triads.

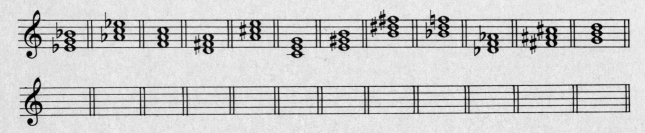

5. Add a note above each given tone to form perfect fifths.

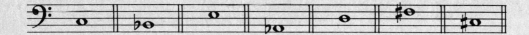

6. Your answers to No. 5 should look like the following. Now insert a third in between each of these fifths, thereby forming minor triads.

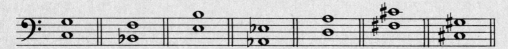

7. Identify all of the triads below as major, minor, augmented, or diminished.

8. Use the tones given below for practice in constructing various types of triads. Do not write the triads down, but recite the letter names of the pitches involved in each instance, according to the following scheme:

$$\text{The given pitch as } \begin{Bmatrix} \text{root} \\ \text{third} \\ \text{fifth} \end{Bmatrix} \text{ of a } \begin{Bmatrix} \text{major} \\ \text{minor} \\ \text{augmented} \\ \text{diminished} \end{Bmatrix} \text{ triad.}$$

Examples:

"F sharp is the root of a minor triad; the triad is F sharp, A, C sharp."

"F sharp is the third of a major triad; the triad is D, F sharp, A."

"F sharp is the fifth of an augmented triad; the triad is B flat, D, F sharp."

This exercise lends itself to a buddy system: have a fellow student drill you by specifying the factors and triadic types, while you spell out the notes; switch your roles from time to time. The exercise can also be used in this way in ear training at the piano.

Return to this exercise as frequently as you can, until you have mastered it in all its variations.

9. Construct major, minor, augmented, and diminished triads, in that order, above each of the given notes.

Example

10. In each of the following fragments, locate the root of the triad. Recite the letter names of the triadic factors, and determine whether each triad is major, minor, augmented, or diminished. (N.B.: Two of these fragments contain tones that are not members of their surrounding chords.) Don't write out your answers; use this example for oral practice instead, returning to it as often as necessary.

SECTION C

Programmed Series

1. Examine all the pitches in the lower part of the following example. What is the pre-vailing triad?

Beethoven, *Sonata*, Op. 7, IV

---

2. Name the principal tones of the melody in the first two measures of the upper part. What triad do they outline?

---

3. Examine all the other tones in the upper part. To what triad do they belong?

4. The following familiar excerpt is in what key?

Verdi, *La Traviata*, Act I

Li - bia - mo, li - bia - mo, ne' lie - ti ca - li - ci,

5. What triad is the basis of the previous excerpt?

6. Indicate all the nonchord tones in the excerpt.

7. In what key is the following excerpt?

Wagner, *Tannhäuser*

8. What triad is the principal chord in the previous excerpt?

9. Indicate precisely all nonchord tones.

10. Is the use of nonchord tones in the excerpt more or less extensive than the use of chord tones?

11. The Chopin excerpt below contains a greater number of different chords than the previous excerpts in this section. Reduced chords in root position have been given in

small notes below some of these harmonies to show the triads in their simplest form.
Write in the remaining reduced chords in the blank space provided.

Chopin, *Prelude*, Op. 28, No. 9

*Ignore this note for now. After Chapter 8 you will be able to explain it.

---

12. The rhythmic pattern given below coincides with the different harmonies in the Chopin excerpt. Below each note, indicate whether the triad represented is major, minor, augmented, or diminished.

---

13. Now identify the triads by their appropriate roman numerals.

---

14. One tone in the bass melody is not a chord tone. Which one is it?

---

15. The passage by Purcell given below is provided for practice in the identification of triads in music. In the blank staff write reduced chords (in root position) for each successive harmony.

Purcell: *Suite No. 1*, Prelude

16. Identify the quality (major, minor, etc.) of each triad used in the excerpt above, giving your answers here:

17. Label each chord in the foregoing question with a roman numeral according to its function in the key of G major.

Be sure that you understand all the material presented thus far in Unit Two. If you aren't certain, review. Then continue; this is one of the longest sections and it will provide you with a firm foundation for future study.

18. The excerpt below with six flats in its signature is in the key of _____ major.

Schubert, *Impromptu*, Op. 90, No. 3

19. There are a total of _____ different triads in this excerpt.

20. The first triad is a I, and it is a major triad. The second is a _____ and it is a _____ triad.

21. The top line is somewhat static: four B flats and a G flat only. Nevertheless, it is the principal melody in this small portion of the composition; much of our attention as we hear the piece is given to this line. Its prominence is due somewhat to the fact

that it is the top voice. In four-part writing, the top part is called the _____ .

22. Copy the soprano of the excerpt into the blank staff below.

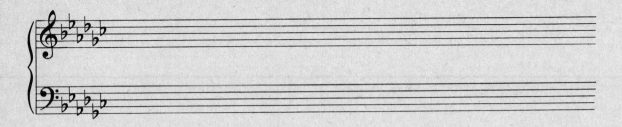

23. The bottom line (bass) of the excerpt is somewhat similar to the soprano. Write it in the lower staff in No. 22 above.

24. Add the next-to-lowest part. In four-part writing, this is called the _____ .

25. Now consider the alto part alone. Even though it has a lot of notes, it consists entirely of chord tones. On the staff below, write out the different chord tones in order of their appearance, eliminating repeated chord tones. (The barline comes between the two separate harmonies.)

26. Write these chord tones as two three-part chords, fitting them into what you already have of the construct with the three parts in No. 22 above.

27. Now we have a six-voice construct. Are all six parts essential? Some of the parts are in fact identical, except for their octave placement. Let us delete one of these doubling parts, such as the "contralto" part, which is an octave below the soprano part. (Of course, we could leave the contralto part and delete the soprano instead; but because the soprano is prominent as the melody, and the doubling voice below it is subsidiary to it, we should preferably delete the doubling voice.)

28. The process above leaves five parts, and we can simplify it further by deleting the next-to-lowest, which is a doubling of the middle part. This will leave four parts in a normal spacing, three in the upper staff and one in the lower.

(These four parts can now be called by the normal names—soprano, alto, tenor, and bass—which would have been confusing when there were six parts.)

The foregoing process of reduction serves as a simple illustration of how a somewhat complex musical texture may be simplified so as to show its essential harmonic action, in which the basic motions of the constituent parts are made apparent.

---

29. The Chopin excerpt below was studied earlier in this section. Let us consider now whether it is possible to derive an SATB construct from it. On the blank staves underneath, copy down the outer parts, while merging repeated tones in either part into single tones, and eliminating any nonchord tones.

Chopin, *Prelude*, Op. 28, No. 9

---

30. Now cross out the second of each triplet eighth-note group of the remaining figuration (nearly all of these merely duplicate the pitches of the top part). Merge the repeated tones in what is left into single quarter notes, and write them here:

31. Combine the upper and lower parts of No. 29 with what you just did in No. 30. (Write it down in No. 29 above.)

32. What you now have should look like the following (the tie marks are optional):

33. So that your construct will more nearly resemble a textbook example of four-part writing, rewrite No. 32 an octave higher.

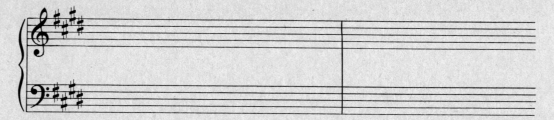

Use this construct to check doubling, ranges, and spacing. Does the SATB realization suggest that the composer has utilized preferred doubling? Do the voices of the construct show good spacing?

34. More excerpts are given below for additional practice or study. The following steps are suggested as a guide in working with each example:

a. Identify the tonality of the excerpt.

b. Provide a three-part, root-position triadic reduction for each harmony, on a separate staff.

c. Label each chord with a roman numeral indicating its function in the key.

d. Cross out all nonchord tones.

e. Merge successive repeated tones into single tones; where necessary, fill up rest spaces by extending the duration of preceding tones.

f. Where appropriate, reduce the texture to four parts by eliminating lines that merely duplicate other lines and/or pitches.

g. As necessary, raise or lower any or all parts an octave, so that the construct will correspond with the usual SATB format and register.

h. Summarize your findings in a paragraph, taking note of range, spacing, and doubling, and note any agreement between the excerpt and the preferred usages as described in your main text.

reduced
chords:

SATB
construct:

Summary of findings:

Beethoven, *Alla Ingharese, Quasi un Capriccio* (The Rage Over a Lost Penny, Vented in a Caprice), Op. 129

reduced
chords:

SATB
construct:

Summary of findings:

reduced
chords:

SATB
construct:

Summary of findings:

Slowly

reduced
chords:

SATB
construct

Summary of findings:

reduced
chords:

SATB
construct:

Summary of findings:

Andante mosso

Ad - di - o___ del pas - sa - to___ bei___

reduced
chords:

SATB
construct:

Summary of findings:

Composition Activities

---

1. Write a phrase four measures long based entirely on tonic harmony in F major, utilizing the following accompanimental pattern for piano combined with a melody in the low register for a gently moving legato bass instrument of your choice (cello, bassoon, baritone saxophone, etc.). The tempo should be slow (*Lento*) or moderately slow (*Andante*).

2. Write another phrase under the same conditions, except that the melody will be in the middle register, like an inner part, and in constant motion. Choose a middle-register instrument such as a viola, tenor or alto saxophone, clarinet, or horn.

3. In a final version of the same pattern, write a lyrical, distinctive melody in the upper register in moderate tempo (*Andante con moto; Allegretto*) for flute, oboe, clarinet, or violin.

4. Write a phrase anywhere from three to eight measures long for trumpet and piano, E-flat major, 3/4 time, quick tempo, using the given measure as a model for the accompaniment. Use only tonic harmony throughout. The trumpet part should be spirited and incisive and should stress the factors of the tonic triad (E flat, G, B flat), although it may use other tones as well. Be certain to write in all dynamic, phrasing, and articulation markings into both parts.

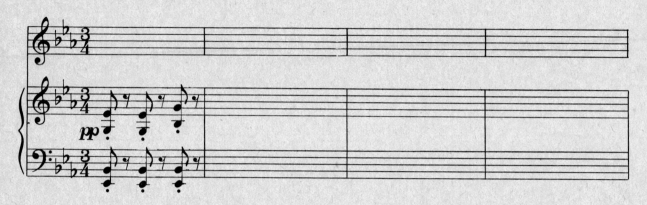

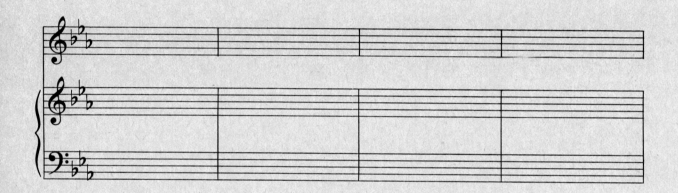

5. Search through the standard repertory of piano music and find six different examples of *left-hand* patterns that unmistakably project a single root-position harmony in a way that is pianistically characteristic, and copy them down. Typical examples would be the well-known kind of oom-pah-pah waltz accompaniment,

or this kind of arpeggiation:

Having done this, compose *three* such patterns, each four measures long, that are more or less similar to the ones you have found, and add a suitable right-hand melody.

SECTION E

Self Test

1. Any simultaneous sounding of two or more harmonic intervals is called a

    _____ .

2. The _____ is the simplest chord, built of three tones.

3. The triad results from the superposition of two _____ .

4. The factors of any triad are referred to as the _____ , the _____ ,

    and the _____ .

5. When the root is not the lowest tone the chord is said to be _____ .

6. The _____ of the triad is in the lowest voice when the chord is in second inversion.

7. When the third of the triad is the lowest tone, the chord is said to be in _____ inversion.

8. The four basic types of triads are major, _____ , _____ , and _____ .

9. Between its root and its other factors, a major triad always has the intervals of a _____ third and a _____ fifth.

10. The _____ triad always has a minor third and a diminished fifth between the root and the other tones.

11. The augmented triad has a _____ _____ and a _____ fifth between the root and the other tones.

12. In what ways are major and minor triads alike? In what ways are they different?

   _____

   _____

13. The _____ and _____ triads are consonant.

14. The _____ and _____ triads are dissonant.

15. In any major key, major triads are found on the _____ , _____ , and _____ degrees.

16. On II, III, and VI in any major key the triads are _____ .

17. The triad on VII of any major key is always _____ .

18. An augmented triad _____ available diatonically in any major key.

is / is not

19. The names customarily applied to the individual parts in four-part writing are: _____ , _____ , _____ , and _____ .

20. In four-part writing, the duplication of one of the triadic factors in order to obtain a fourth part is called _____ .

21. The _____ is usually selected to be doubled in a root-position triad.

22. The leading-tone usually _____ doubled when the VII triad is used.

is / is not

23. The commonest arrangement of the notes in an SATB construct is to have the _____ intervals on the bottom, with the _____ intervals toward the top.

Harmonic Progression in the Major Mode: Rules of Voice Leading

---

SECTION A
Words to Know

Define and memorize:

harmonic progression	direct motion	overlapping	contrary motion
common tone	leading-tone resolution	direct fifths	parallel motion
linear movement	similar motion	conjunct	false relation
disjunct	hidden fifths	stepwise	crossing
oblique motion			

Contrast:

strong progressions/weak progressions

SECTION B
Technical Exercises

Preliminary Remarks: Unless specific instructions are given to the contrary, all the exercises of this section are to be worked out note against note (Latin, *punctus contra punctum*), that is, with all the added parts having the same rhythmic values as the respective given notes.

1. Following Rule of Thumb 1 (text, page 24) precisely, work out each of the progressions below in four parts. Be very careful about doubling and spacing. Indicate the key of each progression, and provide a root analysis by writing in the appropriate roman numerals.

Example

D: V   I

2. Complete each of the following in four parts, departing from Rule of Thumb 1 to the extent of not retaining the common tone in the same voice. Be careful to avoid prohibited motion in voice leading, and be sure to observe proper doubling. Indicate the key and provide a root analysis for each progression.

3. The harmonic progression IV–V is perhaps the most common progression of chords not sharing common tones. Work out the following examples in four parts, applying Rule of Thumb 2 (text, page 25):

4. A regular exception to Rule of Thumb 2 is the V–VI progression, especially when the leading-tone in the soprano resolves up by step to the tonic, the third of VI then being doubled. (See text, page 25.) Work out the following examples in the spaces provided, in each case with the leading-tone in the soprano of V, so that the exception applies. Then on the blank staves underneath, work them out again with the leading-tone in an inner voice (alto or tenor), in such a way that the exception does not apply (in other words, so that Rule of Thumb 2 is strictly followed).

F: V   VI   V   VI   V   VI   V   VI   V   VI

5. Number each of the fragments below according to the type of motion observed. Use the following key:

       1—contrary motion   3—similar motion
       2—oblique motion   4—parallel motion

N.B. The rules governing direct motion to a fifth or octave distinguish between two situations: one, when both voices skip, and two, where one voice skips and the other steps.

Although skipping in both voices to an octave or fifth is avoided as a rule, it is always allowed (text, page 31, Exception 1) when a single harmony changes spacing or position (text, Example 3-26), and it regularly occurs as a generally accepted special case (page 31, Exception 2) in the progression V–I under suitable restrictions (Example 3-27). In neither of these cases should the skips involve both outer voices.

The second situation, direct motion to an octave or fifth with one voice skipping and the other stepping, is always permitted between any pair of voices, *except* when the bass steps and the soprano skips:

C: IV   V   V⁶   I   IV   V

6. With the above constraints in mind, examine the progressions below and determine what types of direct motion to an octave or fifth they contain. Where the direct motion is of the incorrect type, mark it with wavy lines; where it is correct, mark it with dotted lines.

Example

(a special problem here?)

(As a further exercise, perhaps for classroom discussion at the blackboard, consider the various ways in which the incorrect measures might be rectified.)

7. Complete each of the following in four parts, in each case including one chord with a doubled third or fifth, or with omitted fifth.

F: C: G:

8. Work out the following according to the Rules of Thumb, but divide the upper parts into quarter-note values so as to obtain a different spacing for the final chord.

E: G♭ :   B:

9. The following bass lines are slightly longer than those you have done up to now. Doubling of tones other than the root may be employed, but not more often than twice per exercise. (Remember not to double the leading-tone in V. More will be said about doubling in Chapter 6 of your main text.) Rhythmic subdivision of the upper parts will also be allowed in these exercises, with the restriction that not more than two notes in any upper part per note of the bass line should be used.

10. The bass line given below is the root succession, not the actual bass line, of the opening measures of Chopin's well-known *Prelude in D-flat major*, often called "Raindrop." Add three upper parts above this bass, note against note, forming triads in root position. To achieve variety, from time to time you should change from open position to close position, or vice versa.

11. Now write another root-position harmonization of this same bass, this time with the upper parts moving freely to change position or spacing, though without using any note values shorter than a quarter note.

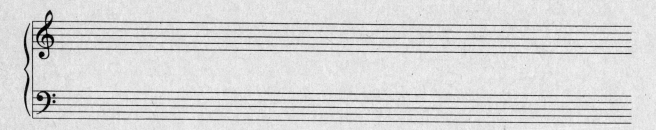

12. The following longer exercises are derived from actual examples in the literature. Work them out according to restrictions specified by your teacher, or by you yourself.

Schubert, Impromptu, Op. 90, No. 4

Allegretto

Andante

(Ländlertempo)

Schubert, *Ländler*, from Op. 18 (adapted)

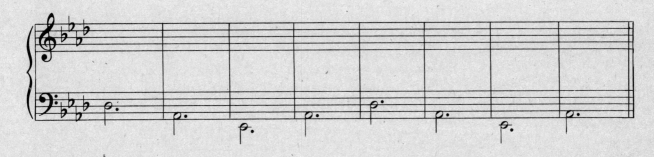

Kuhlau, *Sonatina*, Op. 55, No. 4, II (adapted)

Andante con espressione

p sostenuto

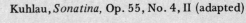

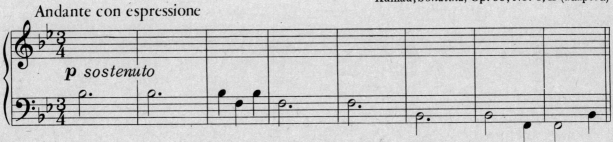

Beethoven, *Sonata*, Op. 13 ("Pathétique"), II (adapted)

Adagio cantabile

Allegro vivace

Schumann, *Dichterliebe*, Op. 48: No. 3, *Die Rose, die Lilie, die Taube, die Sonne*

Munter

Dvořák, *Slavonic Dance*, Op. 46, No. 5 (adapted)

Allegro vivace

SECTION C
Programmed Series

1. Examine the following excerpt. What key is it in?

Haydn, *String Quartet*, Op. 33, No. 2, II

2. Renotate the above on two staves, treble and bass clefs, like an SATB score, omitting the upbeat.

3. Working on what you have just written down in No. 2 above, complete the following:
  a) delete all nonchord tones, replacing them as need be with rests;
  b) fill up the rest spaces with tones that are harmonically implied by having been previously sounded, and connect them with appropriate tie marks.

4. Merge all repeated tones into single durations by using tie marks. When you have done all this, the result should look like the following:

5. Now arrest the second-violin figuration by reducing it to chords made up of triadic factors, as you did with the eighth-note patterns in your reduction of the Schubert *Impromptu in G flat* in Unit 2. Do the same for the arpeggiated melody notes in the first-violin part. Adjust all the notation so that most of the tied notes will appear in notes of familiar time value. Recopy the results on the staves below.

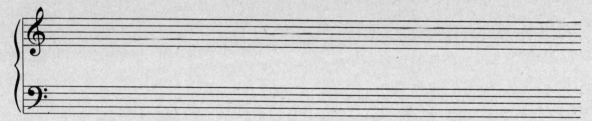

6. The result should look like the following:

or, one step further along:

7. Combine all upper parts, writing the first-violin parts an octave lower. Unison pitches will be represented by single notes.

8. The above is a construct of six parts, in relatively close texture. Two of these parts are obvious doublings an octave below the uppermost melody; they may be deleted.

What now remains is a very simplified scheme which shows, almost abstractly, the harmonic action that serves as a background to Haydn's three measures.

9. What is the key of the following excerpt?

Paine, *A Christmas Gift*

10. Identify the harmonies in the above excerpt by writing in roman numerals; list them here also. _____

11. Rewrite the excerpt above, omitting the lowest line of notes, since its function is merely to add depth to the sound by duplicating another part. Also, in the second measure eliminate the line that is a duplication of the top melody.

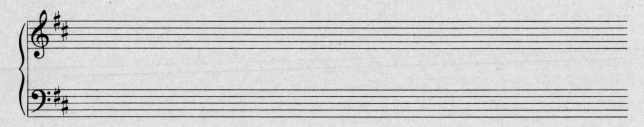

12. The new version, your answer to No. 11 above, has not altered the harmony at all. Simplify it further by leaving out the pickup note and all nonchord tones. Where nonchord tones are omitted, extend the duration of the notes preceding. Rewrite below, using the customary SATB format.

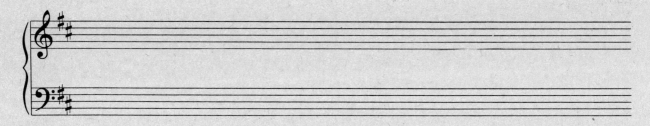

13. Your final version should look like the following:

Observe the spacing. Is it proper spacing? Which factor of each separate chord is doubled—root, third, or fifth? In the tonic chord in the first full measure, there is a perfect fifth between S and T, approached in similar motion with skips in both voices; why is this not considered objectionable motion in this case?

SECTION D
Composition Activities

1. On a separate piece of manuscript paper, copy out the following accompanimental pattern, leaving a blank staff above. Extend the pattern through three measures of subdominant and tonic triads, as indicated. (Don't change the spacing; apply Rule of Thumb 1, so as to obtain minimal motion. The lowest voice is to be considered a textural duplication of the bass line throughout this five-part pattern.) Then compose a melody for solo voice, writing it on the blank staff. Be sure to include a suitable text.

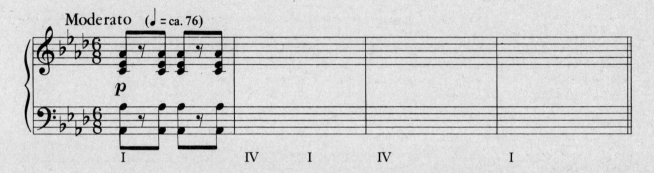

2. Continue the accompanimental pattern of the piano excerpt given below, while inventing an original continuation of the melody also. Follow the chord pattern indicated. The extension of the melody should have essentially the same note values as in the given measure; this will lend rhythmic unity to the passage.

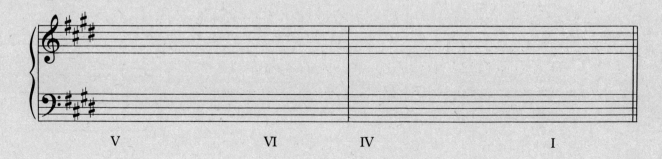

3. Work out the following in rhythmic unison, according to the rhythm and root progressions given. Move the upper parts up or down fairly freely as you wish, but keep them always in close position. Choose a suitable tempo and dynamics. Score for three clarinets and bass clarinet.

4. Using the given measure as a beginning, write several extensions according to the rhythms and measure lengths indicated.

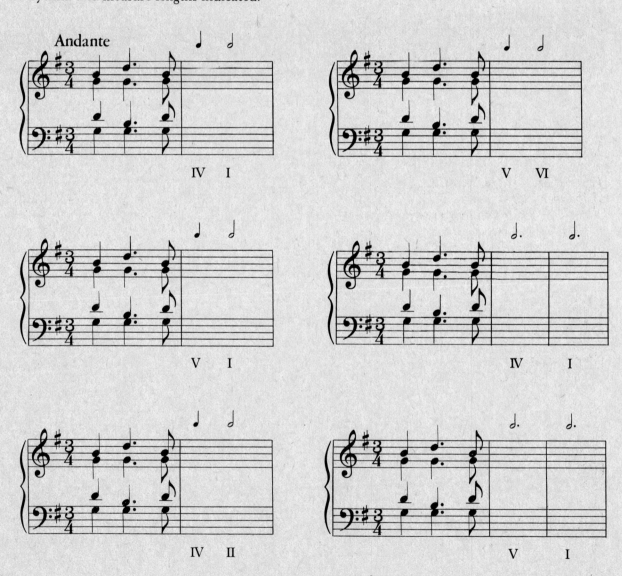

IV II   V VI

5. Extend the given measure according to the indicated patterns, as in No. 4 above.
(Adapted from Schubert, *Impromptu,* Op. 142, No. 3.)

Andante

Bb: I   IV V   I V   I

Bb: I   VI   II   V

B: I   VI III   V   V I

B: I   V   I IV I

53

6. Compose a fanfare, *Maestoso*, for two trumpets and two trombones, on the harmonic pattern indicated below. The rhythm will be your own choice, but all parts must proceed in rhythmic unison.

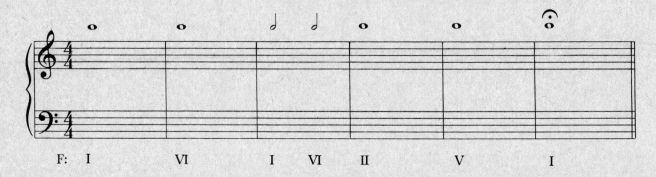

F: I   VI   I   VI   II   V   I

SECTION E
Self Test

1. Harmonic progressions may be classified according to the relative distances between the _____ of the triads involved.

2. The harmonic progression II–V is an example of a root succession that is _____ used.
<u>frequently / infrequently</u>

3. The progression from II to V would be classified as a _____ progression.
<u>strong / weak</u>

4. The harmonic progression involving root succession with movement up a third is considered usually to be _____ .
<u>strong / weak</u>

5. Root successions by upward step, upward perfect fifth, or upward perfect fourth are relatively _____ in music.
<u>common / uncommon</u>

6. Voice leading is the means whereby one chord is _____ to another.

7. State Rule of Thumb 1 in your own words. _____

_____

_____

8. What is the common exception to Rule of Thumb 1? _____

_____

9. State Rule of Thumb 2 in your own words. _____

_____

_____

10. What progression is the common exception to Rule of Thumb 2? _____

_____

11. On occasion, it is possible or even desirable to omit the _____ of a triad, and to _____ its root.

12. It is generally undesirable to omit the _____ of a triad, because it leaves the open sound of the _____ .

13. Does the change of position of a chord, without other intervening chords sounding, constitute a harmonic progression? _____

14. What is a tritone? Why is it so called? _____

15. Define overlapping voices. _____

_____

_____

The Minor Mode

SECTION A
Words to Know

Define and memorize:

natural minor
parallel minor
augmented second
harmonic minor

melodic minor
augmented mediant
relative minor

Contrast:

ascending melodic minor / descending melodic minor

SECTION B
Technical Exercises

1. Assume that each note given below is the keynote of a major scale. Write in the keynote of the relative minor.

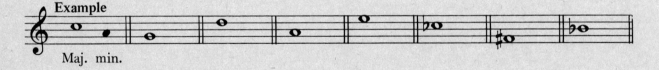

Maj. min.

2. The keynotes to various minor scales are written below. Write in the keynote of the relative major scale for each of these minors.

min. Maj.

3. Circle each pair of successive tones that form a half step in each of the following scale segments. Then determine the particular natural minor scale that is hidden in each succession and identify it by putting an **X** through each keynote.

4. Without altering the initial keynotes, add accidentals to the following segments so as to transform them into natural minor scales.

5. Give the letter name of the keynote of each natural minor scale indicated by the following key signatures:

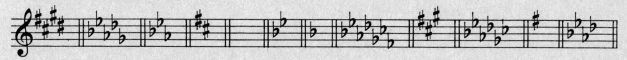

6. In the following successions of whole and half steps, the keynotes of natural minor scales are given. Write in the names of the other tones needed to complete each scale.

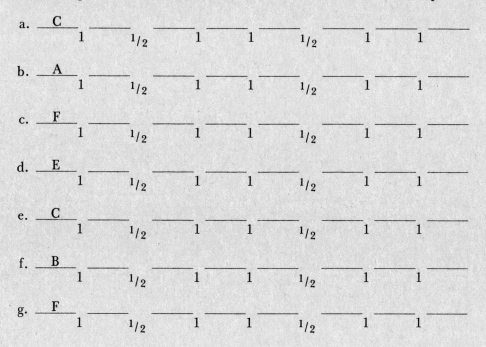

a. __C__ _____ _____ _____ _____ _____ _____
      1   ¹/₂   1   1   ¹/₂   1   1

b. __A__ _____ _____ _____ _____ _____ _____
      1   ¹/₂   1   1   ¹/₂   1   1

c. __F__ _____ _____ _____ _____ _____ _____
      1   ¹/₂   1   1   ¹/₂   1   1

d. __E__ _____ _____ _____ _____ _____ _____
      1   ¹/₂   1   1   ¹/₂   1   1

e. __C__ _____ _____ _____ _____ _____ _____
      1   ¹/₂   1   1   ¹/₂   1   1

f. __B__ _____ _____ _____ _____ _____ _____
      1   ¹/₂   1   1   ¹/₂   1   1

g. __F__ _____ _____ _____ _____ _____ _____
      1   ¹/₂   1   1   ¹/₂   1   1

7. Write out natural minor scales for the keynotes indicated below. Do not use key signatures, but insert the appropriate accidental signs beside the notes as needed.

8. In the following successions of intervals, the keynotes of harmonic minor scales are given. Write in the names of the other tones needed to complete each scale.

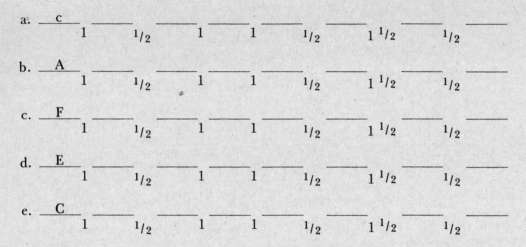

a. __c__ ___ ___ ___ ___ ___ ___ ___
    1   ½   1   1   ½   1 ½   ½

b. __A__ ___ ___ ___ ___ ___ ___ ___
    1   ½   1   1   ½   1 ½   ½

c. __F__ ___ ___ ___ ___ ___ ___ ___
    1   ½   1   1   ½   1 ½   ½

d. __E__ ___ ___ ___ ___ ___ ___ ___
    1   ½   1   1   ½   1 ½   ½

e. __C__ ___ ___ ___ ___ ___ ___ ___
    1   ½   1   1   ½   1 ½   ½

9. Write the harmonic minor scales for each of the following keynotes. Use the ordinary key signatures and write in the appropriate accidental for the seventh degree.

10. Write the ascending and descending forms of the melodic minor scales for the given keynotes. Do not use key signatures, but write in accidentals where required.

11. Without using key signatures, write out the triads found in each harmonic minor scale indicated by the keynotes given below. Label each triad according to whether it is major, minor, etc.

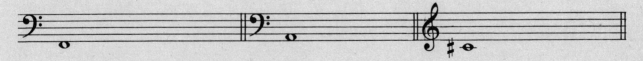

12. Since in any harmonic minor scale I and IV are minor triads, V and VI are major, II and VII are diminished, and III is augmented:

the triad C–E♭–G may be found on (for example) __IV__ in __G__ harmonic minor,

and on _____ in _____ harmonic minor;

the triad C–E–G may be found on _____ in _____ harmonic minor,

and on _____ in _____ harmonic minor;

the triad C–E–G♯ may be found on _____ in _____ harmonic minor,

and on _____ in _____ harmonic minor;

the triad C–E♭–G♭ is always found on _____ in _____ harmonic minor,

and on _____ in _____ harmonic minor.

13. Each of the following triads may be found in more than one harmonic minor scale. Determine the structural type of each triad and name all the scales in which each will be found.

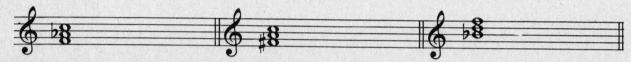

14. Write down the triads indicated, using accidental signs and omitting key signatures. Derive the triads from the harmonic minor scale only.

15. Provide a four-part harmonization for each of the following derived bass lines, using root-position triads only, note against note. The seventh degree will be major in the dominant chords. Be careful to avoid the melodic interval of augmented second.

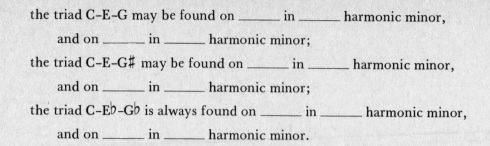

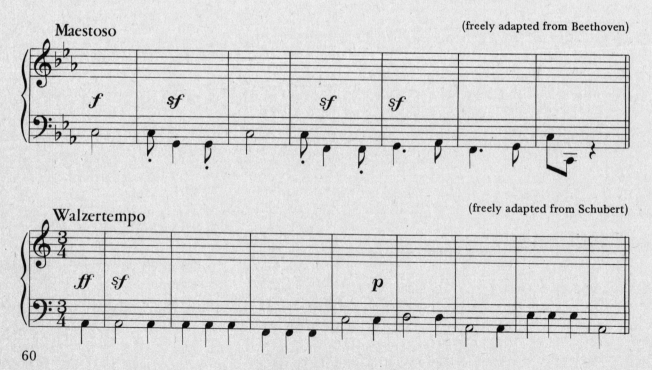

SECTION C
Programmed Series

1. Identify the key of the following excerpt; label each chord and identify its type (major, minor, etc.).

Mendelssohn, *Violin Concerto*, Op. 64, I

2. Write out the scale that is the basis of the preceding example.

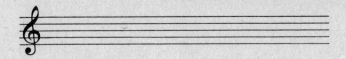

3. Respectively, the sixth and seventh degrees of this scale are _____ and _____ (name the notes). The form of the scale in No. 2 above is accordingly _____ minor.

4. Does the sixth degree also appear in its raised form, C#? _____

5. Does the minor seventh degree (subtonic) ever appear in the excerpt? _____

6. In the excerpt given below, the presence of both C sharp and C natural, together with B flat and B natural, sometimes suggests the melodic minor mode, or a mixture of minor forms. The keynote (tonic) of this excerpt is _____ .

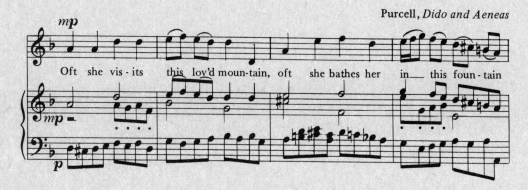

Purcell, *Dido and Aeneas*

Oft she vis-its this lov'd moun-tain, oft she bathes her in__ this foun-tain

7. For study purposes, extract the third measure of the bass of the above.

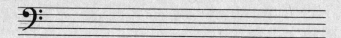

8. Write here the three forms of the D-minor scale:

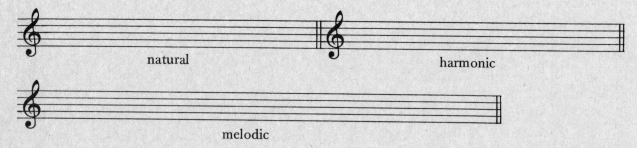

natural   harmonic

melodic

9. In the measure you extracted in No. 7 above, examine the B natural. From which form of the minor does this tone come? _____

10. What is the direction of motion away from this B natural? _____

11. The C sharp is immediately followed by the dominant note, A; however, we also sense that the C sharp is moving upward to the D that follows. The minor seventh degree (C natural) moves _____ to the B flat and then continues in the same direction.

12. The major seventh degree, the leading-tone C sharp, in the first measure moves _____ to the _____ note.

13. In the second half of the third measure, the C natural and B flat in the bass belong to the _____ form of the minor scale.

14. What can you say about the sixth and seventh degrees of the minor scale as they are used in the fourth measure of the excerpt? _____

_____

15. The following excerpt is in the key of _____ , and the form of the minor mode used is the _____ .

Beethoven, Sonata, Op. 27, No. 2 (Sonata quasi una Fantasia), III

16. Rewrite the preceding excerpt, merging all successive repeated tones into single durations.

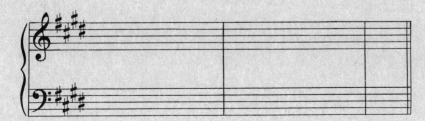

17. Now reduce the above still more, raising the bass voice an octave, removing doubling voices, and moving some tones "to the left" to fill up rest spaces. You should eventually arrive at an SATB construct like the following:

I $\begin{smallmatrix}6\\4\end{smallmatrix}$

18. Label all the chords in this construct, except the first chord in the second measure, which is already done for you. (This tonic six-four chord will be dealt with in Chapter 11.) What can you say about the motion of the individual voices in the construct, from chord to chord? What can you say about the doubling? _____

_____

_____

19. Here are some more excerpts for additional study of the uses of the minor mode. Examine each one carefully to determine the particular scale or scales used. Consider whether the composition is based solely upon the harmonic or natural minor, or whether the melodic minor with its major sixth and seventh degrees is involved. Give some attention to the chord progressions themselves: spacing, doubling, voice leading, and the general principles of good chord connection that you learned in Chapter 3. Note down your observations in the space provided below each excerpt.

Mozart, *Violin Sonata*, K. 304, I

Observations:

Observations:

Handel, *Harpsichord Suite No. 11*, III, *Sarabande*

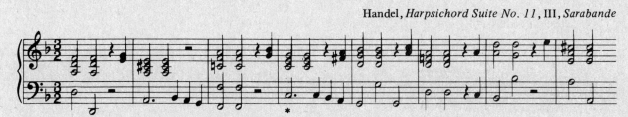

*Read ahead in Chapter 5 of your main text (pp. 59–61) for a fuller explanation of this chord.

Observations:

Schumann, *Album for the Young*,
Op. 68: No. 6, *The Poor Orphan Child*

*See the footnote to the previous excerpt.

Observations:

Composition Activities

1. The following measure, borrowed from Schubert,

is to be used as the first measure of each of four four-measure phrases. Three of these phrases will have one harmony per measure:

while the fourth phrase will have two harmonies per measure in the last three measures, thus:

IV   II   II   V   V   I

2. Write a slow, mournful melody for solo oboe, mostly *p* to *pp*, not more than twelve measures long of either 2/4 or 6/8 meter, and based entirely on the following scale:

3. Using the following scale as a basis,

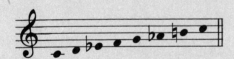

compose an original melody in a happy, dancelike mood, for clarinet. Use 3/4 or 6/8 meter, a lively tempo, mezzoforte intensity level, with accents added as appropriate.

Self Test

1. The letter names of the scale degrees of F-natural minor are: _____ , _____ , _____ , _____ , _____ , _____ , and _____ .

2. The natural minor scale has the same signature as the _____ scale.

3. The keynote of the natural minor is a _____ third _____ the keynote of its relative major.

4. The keynote of any major scale is a _____ third _____ the keynote of the natural minor scale with the same key signature.

5. Is it true or false that on occasion all minor scale forms may be found within the same composition, or even within a section of a composition? _____

6. The particular scale degree that differentiates the natural minor scale from the harmonic minor scale having the same tonic is the _____ degree.

7. The harmonic minor differs from the natural minor in that the _____ degree is _____ .

8. The harmonic minor differs from the major scale having the same tonic in its _____ and _____ degrees. These are _____ than in the major.

higher / lower

9. Compared to the natural minor, the ascending form of the melodic minor on the same keynote has the _____ and _____ degrees _____ .

10. The descending melodic minor is _____ from the natural minor.

different / no different

11. If the _____ degree of the major is lowered, the scale becomes identical to the melodic minor, ascending.

12. In constructing harmony, the _____ form of the minor scale will most frequently be considered.

13. The augmented triad on the mediant degree in the minor mode is _____ encountered in music.

frequently / infrequently

14. The principles of voice leading that govern correct harmonic progression and chord connection in the minor mode are _____ those of the major mode.

essentially the same as / fundamentally different from

Tonality and Modality

SECTION A
Words to Know

Define and memorize:

modal scales
mixed modes
Picardy third
tonality
modality
tonicize, tonicization
Dorian
Phrygian

Lydian
Mixolydian
Aeolian
Ionian
pentatonic scale
whole-tone scale
"Hungarian" scale

Contrast:

relative major/relative minor
harmonic minor/major
melodic minor/natural minor
melodic minor/major
chromatic/diatonic

dominant/secondary dominant
tonality/modality
key/scale
tonal degrees/modal degrees

SECTION B
Technical Exercises

1. The "diatonic circle" below is useful in determining the various modal scales. The starting point is indicated for each of the modes, whose intervallic succession is then read in a clockwise direction around the circle.

Study the diagram carefully, and then answer the questions that follow.

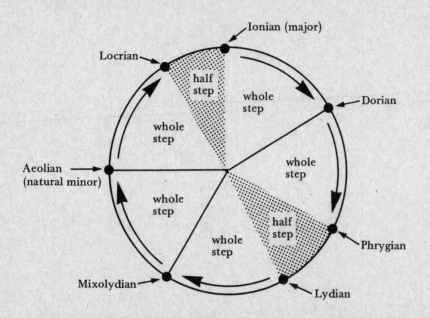

The pattern of half and whole steps for each mode is:

a. Ionian mode (major) EXAMPLE: __1__ __1__ __1/2__ __1__ __1__ __1__ __1/2__

b. Dorian _____

c. Mixolydian _____

d. Lydian _____

e. Aeolian (natural minor) _____

f. Phrygian _____

2. Write out the pitches of each of the following scales according to the given keynote and scalar type, as shown in the example.

Example

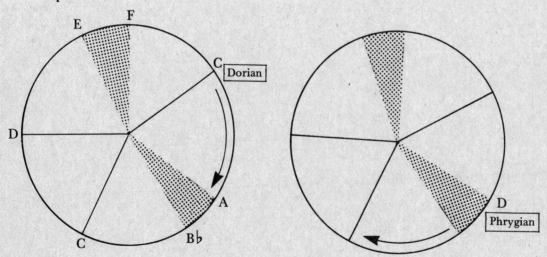

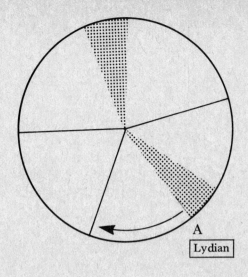

A
Lydian

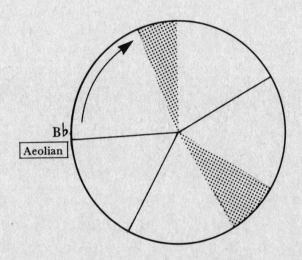

B♭
Aeolian

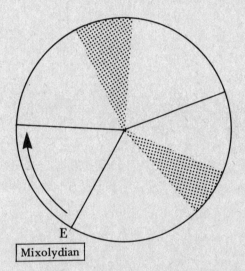

E
Mixolydian

3. For additional practice in constructing modal scales, work on the sequences given below. Don't write out the answers, but recite them out loud, in partnership with a fellow student if you wish. Refer back to the diatonic circle in No. 1 above, if necessary.

a. Starting on C: Dorian, Phrygian, Lydian, Mixolydian, Aeolian.

b. The same modes as above, but starting on: D, F♯, B♭, C♯, E.

c. Dorian, on: C, D, A♭, E♭, G, F.

d. Phrygian, on: A, B, F♯, E♭, C♯, B♭.

e. Lydian, on: C, D, A♭, E, G, F.

f. Mixolydian, on: A, B, F♯, D♭, F, E♭.

g. Aeolian on: F, G, E, A♭, D, C.

71

4. Write out the following modal scales, starting on C:

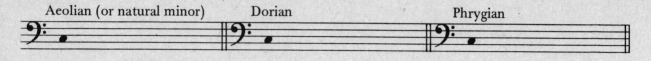

Now compare the scales you have just constructed, and answer the following questions:

    a. How does the Dorian mode specifically differ from the natural minor? _____
_____

    b. How does the Phrygian mode differ from the Aeolian? _____
_____

5. Using C as the keynote, write out the following scales:

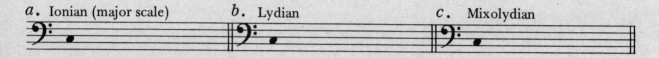

Now answer the following questions about the scales you have just constructed:

    a. In what way is the Lydian mode different from the major? _____
_____

_____

    b. In what way is the Mixolydian mode different from the major? _____
_____

_____

6. Circle all the tonal degrees of the following scales, and cross out all the modal degrees.

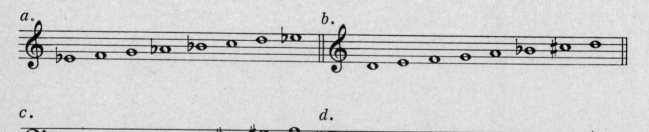

7. Name the tonal degrees of the following scales:

    a. F major: ___ ___ ___ ___

    b. E minor: (harmonic)   ___ ___ ___ ___

    c. D major: ___ ___ ___ ___

    d. B major: ___ ___ ___ ___

    e. D♭ major: ___ ___ ___ ___

    f. A♭ major: ___ ___ ___ ___

    g. C♯ minor: (natural)   ___ ___ ___ ___

    h. E♭ major: ___ ___ ___ ___

    i. C minor (ascending melodic) ___ ___ ___ ___

    j. A major: ___ ___ ___ ___

8. Name the modal degrees of the following scales:

    a. G natural minor: ___ ___   d. C♯ major: ___ ___

    b. G♭ major: ___ ___   e. E major: ___ ___

    c. B♭ major: ___ ___   f. F♯ natural minor: ___ ___

9. In the following melody, circle all the tonal degrees, cross out all the modal degrees, and place a small arrow pointing to each leading-tone.

Bach, *Two-Part Invention No. 1*

10. Complete each of the following in four parts, note against note, according to the given tempos and rhythmic schemes. In each case provide a text to be sung with music. Use a variety of dynamics.

Example   Quickly

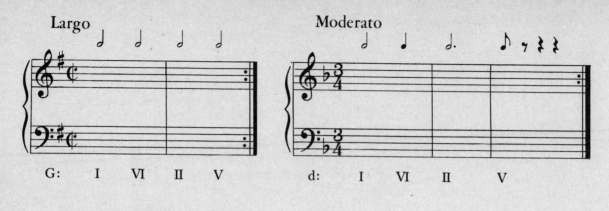

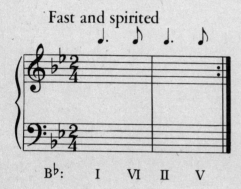

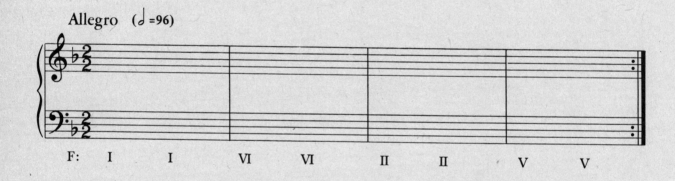

11. Work out a phrase in four parts in D major, note against note, according to the rhythm and harmony shown. Use root position only, and at least one chord borrowed from the minor mode.

74

12. In completing the following, use only root-position triads from the D harmonic-minor scale, and end with a Picardy third. The bass should have the rhythm indicated; all the other parts should move mostly in quarter and eighth notes.

13. The following are to be completed in four freely moving parts, in root position; the rhythms indicated reflect the changes of harmony and do not necessarily apply to any particular part.

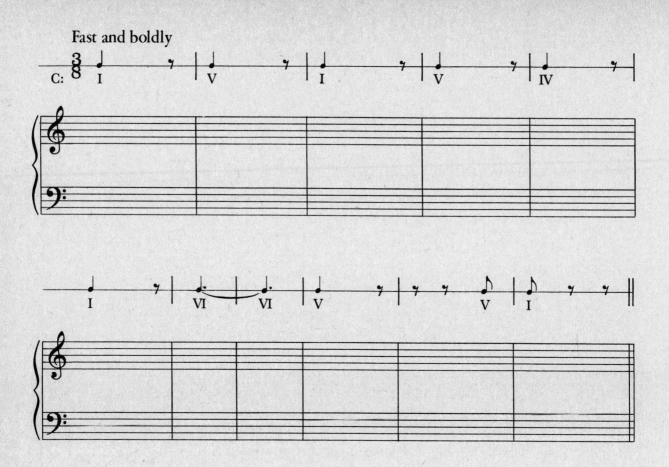

14. Additional practice may be had by varying Exercises 10 through 13 in the following ways:

    a. Rework each exercise, beginning with a different spacing for the first chord.

    b. Keep the same basic progression and meter, but use different rhythms and tempos. Several different versions may be written, as in No. 10 above.

    c. Rework in major those that are at present in minor, and vice versa.

SECTION C

Programmed Series

1. Sing or play this tune until you know it note-perfect, if you don't already.

Traditional American tune, *Ten Little Indians*

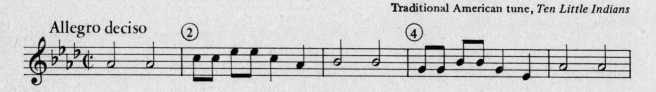

What is the key of this tune? _____ What is its mode? _____

---

2. The pitches at the beginning and end of the tune above, along with the signature of four flats, give strong indication that this melody is in the key of A-flat major. Therefore, A flat is the central tone in this tune. In the blank measures below, write down all the A flats that appear in No. 1.

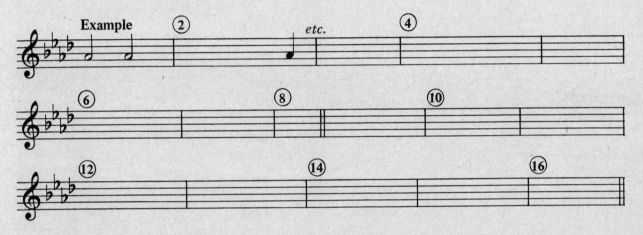

---

3. The pitch A flat appears _____ in this tune, and occupies a relatively

                                  frequently / infrequently

_____ portion of the total duration.

large / small

---

4. Reexamine No. 1 above. Find all the notes on the dominant and write them into the corresponding spaces in No. 2.

---

5. E flat appears in the tune in measures _____ , _____ , _____ , _____ , _____ ,

_____ , _____ , and _____ . Compared to the tonic note it has a relatively

_____ portion of the total duration, and a relatively _____ metrical

large / small   strong / weak

accent.

---

6. How often in this melody does the dominant note immediately precede the tonic? _____ How many times is it separated from the following tonic note by only the third degree of the scale? _____

7. In relation to all the other pitches in the melody, are the tonic and dominant pitches important to this tune? _____

8. What can you say about the proximity of the tonic and dominant notes to each other and how do they relate to the tonality of the whole tune? _____

_____

_____

9. Return now to Frames 1 and 2 and carry down the remaining tonal degrees (the second and fourth degrees).

10. Describe briefly the apparent function of B flat in the melody. _____

_____

_____

11. How many fourth degrees (D flats) did you find? _____ Are there other scale degrees that are either little used or absent entirely? _____ Name them. _____

12. How often in this melody does the second degree (B flat) immediately precede the fifth degree (E flat)? _____

13. What portion of the total number of B flats are connected to the dominant tone by an intervening leading-tone? _____

14. B flat, the second degree, bears the same relationship to E flat that E flat does to the _____ .

15. The above suggests that beyond the pitches used as first and last tones in the melody, the tonality of A flat here depends in part on the interrelationship of the tonal degrees, namely _____ , _____ , and _____ .

28. The principal key in the example below is _____ .

Handel, *Messiah*, Part 2

29. In measures 7, 8, and 9 there is a tonicization of the pitch _____ , which is the

_____ of F minor. What supports this tonicization? _____

_____

30. What happens to the tonicization after that? _____

_____

_____

31. The principal key of the following is _____ .

Bach, *Well-Tempered Clavier, Book I*, Fugue No. 2: subject, countersubject, and episode

32. A departure from the principal key, with a tonicization of _____ , occurs from measure _____ to measure _____ . How is this tonicization primarily brought about? _____

_____

33. The principal key of the "harmonic bass line" below is _____ .

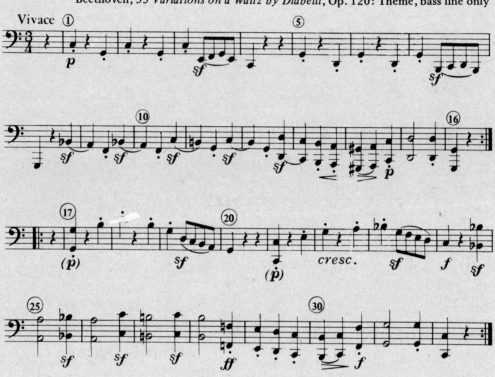

Beethoven, *33 Variations on a Waltz by Diabelli*, Op. 120: Theme, bass line only

34. Taken by itself, this bass line suggests that the following pitches have been tonicized:

Measure number	Pitch
5–8	_____
8–10	_____
15–20	_____
21–26	_____

Composition Activities

---

1. Write a melody for an unaccompanied wind instrument in E♭ major, 6/8 or 3/4 time, slow tempo. Limit the length of your melody to sixteen measures.

2. Write a folk-song-like vocalise for medium-register unaccompanied voice on the syllable *la* or *oo*. Use the natural minor scale on C.

3. Write a twelve-measure beginning of a quiet, meditative, and basically homophonic piece in D major for piano or organ, suitable for use in a church service. Use the following harmonic succession with one harmony per measure:
I–IV–V–I–IV–I–V–VI–IV–II–V–I.
Include some modal mixture.

4. Extend both melody and accompanying parts of the following, using the harmony indicated.

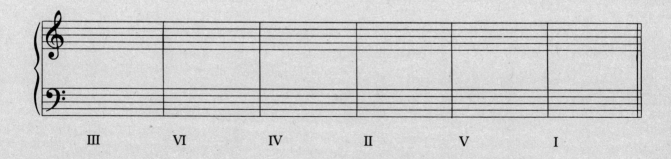

Self Test

1. The word _____ means "the organized relationship of tones in music." (See text, page 47.)

2. Tonality is synonymous with _____ , and modality with _____ .

3. Name the common modal scales, excluding major and natural minor: _____ , . _____ , _____ , and _____ .

4. The Lydian scale _____ be constructed on the pitches G, B flat, C sharp, or
   may / may not
   on any of the other available pitches.

5. The function of the _____ is to be the tonal center.

6. _____ and _____ are the two scale degrees which "seem to give an impression of balanced support to the tonic, like two equidistant weights on either side of a fulcrum." (See text, page 49.)

7. The tonal degrees of any major or minor scale are _____ , _____ , _____ , and _____ .

8. _____ and _____ are the modal degrees of A-flat major.

9. The modal degrees in any major or minor scale are _____ and _____ .

10. The progression V—I, found at the end of a phrase, is called the _____ .

11. Elementary tonal units, that is, groups of two or three chords with distinct meaning as to key, may be referred to as _____ .

12. A change of mode within a composition from major to minor, or vice versa, generally _____ affect the tonality.
    does / does not

13. Interchange of modes is more probable when the prevailing mode is _____ , rather than _____ .

14. When a composition with a prevailing minor mode ends on a major tonic triad, the effect is called _____ .

15. When a tone other than the keynote of the prevailing key is made to be heard momentarily as tonic, the tone is said to be _____ .

16. B major and B minor are said to be _____ modes.

17. Tones that are not members of the diatonic scale of the prevailing tonality are called _____ tones.

The First Inversion–
The Figured Bass

Words and Symbols to Know

Define, memorize:

first inversion
second inversion
figured bass
authentic cadence

5
3

6
3

6̸

6♯, 6♭, 6♮

6
4

6 ————

Technical Exercises

1. The following problems dealing with the realization of figured bass require two answers, in most cases:

    a. write in the pitch actually indicated by each figure; and
    b. write in the pitch or pitches not actually indicated by figures but implied by notational custom. (Doubling pitches need not be included.)

Example:

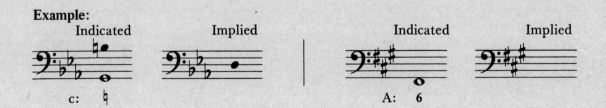

    Indicated   Implied   Indicated   Implied

    c: ♮   A: 6

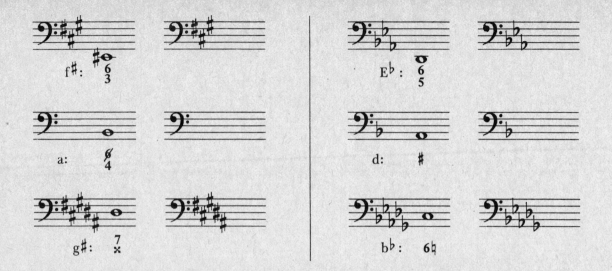

2. Construct triads in four parts, according to the given pitches and figures. Use preferred doubling and spacing, and label each chord.

3. Complete in four parts the progression I—V⁶—I in the keys indicated. Keep common tones in the same voice and move the other voices to their nearest available positions, with only the root being doubled.

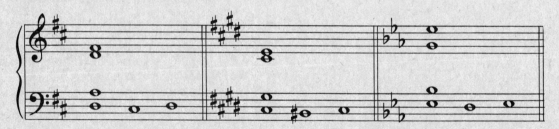

4. Complete two four-part versions of each of the figured basses below. In the first version, common tones are to be kept in the same voice wherever possible, with minimal motion in the other parts; in the second version, the motion may be freer.

5. Realize the following figured bass in four parts, in two versions:

      a. note against note; and
      b. with the upper parts moving freely in quarter notes.

(adapted from Mozart)

Tempo di menuetto

6. Realize the following figured basses in four parts. The upper parts may move freely, note-against-note motion not being required. (In the second figured bass below, *b*, the figures "7" indicate passing-tone sevenths on the second half of the beat; see the definition of the passing tone on page 112 of your main text, and also page 231, Example 15–1.)

Programmed Series

---

1. The key of the following excerpt is _____ .

Beethoven, *Variations on "Ich bin der Schneider Kakadu,"* Op. 121a: Theme

Allegretto

(7)

Label all chords and inversions. (A dominant seventh chord, which we have not yet studied but will consider later in Chapter 15, has already been labeled.)

---

2. Which beats, in which measures, contain tones that do not belong to the prevailing harmony on the beat? _____

---

3. The texture is three part at the beginning; in what measures does the number of parts change? _____

---

4. Certain chords have one factor omitted. Locate these, giving measure and beat numbers, and identify the factor that is omitted (i.e., root, third, or fifth). _____

---

5. The first chords of measures 3 and 4 have tones that are doubled. In the II⁶ chord, the _____ of the chord is doubled; that tone is the _____ degree of the scale, a _____ degree.
   tonal / modal

---

6. In the final tonic chord, which factor is doubled? What scale degree is this tone? Is it a tonal or a modal degree? _____

---

7. The doubling in this brief excerpt is confined to _____ degrees, and if a factor is omitted it is always the _____ of the chord.

89

8. Reduce the four-measure excerpt in Frame 1 to a simpler texture of three or sometimes four parts as you have done in earlier exercises of this type, by eliminating the upbeat, merging repeated tones, and subsuming nonchord tones. (The seventh of the V^7 is considered to be a chord tone.)

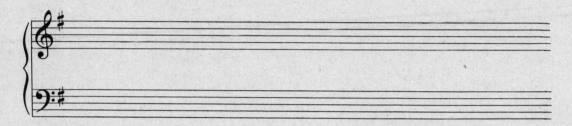

9. Your result should look much like the following, which reveals the underlying harmony more clearly.

Play through this reduction several times, comparing it with the original excerpt as Beethoven wrote it. Below, comment on the use of the V^6 in the first measure.

_____

_____

_____

_____

10. Comment on the use of the II^6 in the third measure. _____

_____

_____

11. In the blank staff below the following excerpt, write close-position triads representing the harmonies used. (In the third and fourth measures a seventh-chord will be necessary.) Write the chords in the same positions or inversions found in the excerpt itself.

Allegro moderato

---

12. Label each of the simple chords above with the appropriate roman- and arabic-numeral notation.

---

13. The II^6 in the excerpt precedes a ——————— chord.

---

14. The root relationship in the progression II^6—V suggests that the II^6 functions herein as a kind of ——————— of the dominant.

---

15. Discuss the relative duration and metrical strength of the II^6 chord as it appears in the excerpt. ———————————————————

———————————————————

———————————————————

———————————————————

---

16. The II^6 has as its root a ——————— degree of the scale.
modal / tonal

---

17. Are the roots of all the triads in the excerpt above tonal degrees? ———————

———————————————————

———————————————————

18. Here is another excerpt for use in practicing your techniques of reduction. Eliminate all duplicating parts and nonchord tones, reducing it to three parts. Use values of whole, half, and quarter notes. Write the reduction on the blank staves underneath.

Mozart, *The Magic Flute*, Act I

Drei Knäb-chen, jung, schön, hold und wei - se, um-schwe - ben uns auf_ uns - rer_ Rei - se.

19. Label all chords in the above with appropriate roman and arabic numerals.

20. Which of these triads are on tonal degrees? On modal degrees?

21. Consider the two chords in the first measure of your reduction. What is the common tone? What factor is the common tone in the first chord? What is it in the second? Describe the motion of the other two voices in the chords.

22. Consider now the second and third measures of the reduction in the same way that you have just considered the first measure. Are there any general similarities? (If you are interested, read ahead in Chapter 9 of your main text, pp. 143–44, Sequence.)

_____

_____

_____

SECTION D

Composition Activities

1. Extend the given measure in three different ways, according to the progressions indicated. Consider the left hand as accompaniment and the right hand as melody. Use some sixteenth notes in the melodic part.

(Use chords of your own choice, but include at least two in the first inversion)

2. Write a keyboard piece based upon the succession of harmonies given below. You may use a freely variable texture of three to seven simultaneous parts, including doubling parts, in a chordal style appropriate to the piano, but written note against note. (The rests given apply to all parts at the moment they occur.)

(freely adapted from Schubert)

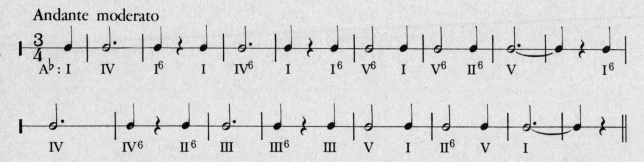

Self Test

1. In the first inversion of a triad, the _____ will be in the bass.

2. _____ is the arabic numeral that indicates that a triad is in the first inversion.

3. Roots are identified by _____ numerals, and inversions by _____ numerals.

4. The abbreviated form for indicating a tonic chord in the first inversion is _____ .

5. A chord labeled II_4^6 is said to be in the _____ inversion.

6. A numeral ^{6} standing alone under a note in a figured bass provides what information, express or implied? _____

7. The choice of the tone for doubling in first-inversion chords is usually decided by what? _____

8. If the bass of a first-inversion triad is *not* a tonal degree, then usually it _____ doubled.

is / is not

9. If a tonal degree is the bass note when a chord is in the first inversion, then this degree _____ usually doubled.

is / is not

10. In a II^6 chord in G major, the preferred tone for doubling purposes is the _____ .

94

11. There _____ new principles of voice leading or of harmonic progression

    are several / are no

    involved in the use of triads in the first inversion.

12. The II^6 is very common at or near the end of a phrase in association with the _____ chord in cadences.

13. III^6 is not usually an independent chord; it is most often the result of a temporary displacement of tones of the _____ chord.

14. The augmented triad in the minor mode appears _____ in first inversion.

    most often / never

15. IV^6 is a useful alternative to _____ when following V, when stepwise motion in the bass is desired.

16. The third of the dominant triad is the _____ of the key.

17. VI^6 often stands in place of the _____ chord.

18. In VII^6 the preferred doubling is of the _____ , though the _____ may also be doubled; on the other hand, the _____ is seldom doubled.

19. The method of denoting upper voices above a given bass note, using arabic numeration, is called _____ .

20. A line drawn vertically or slantwise through an arabic numeral in a figured bass will indicate _____

21. An accidental in isolation below the bass note, not attached to any arabic numeral, always indicates _____

22. A horizontal line following a numeral signifies _____

Function and Structure of Melody

SECTION A
Words to Know

Define and memorize:

melody
theme
countermelody
obbligato
collateral part
cantus firmus
tune
symphonic melody

ostinato
roulade
figuration
anacrusis
motive
phrase
subphrase

antecedent
consequent
arpeggiation
compound melody, compound line
variation
ornamentation, ornament
reduction

Contrast:

theme/tune
tune/symphonic melody
range/contour

SECTION B
Technical Exercises

1. Below is a four-measure excerpt from the full score of Beethoven's *Ninth Symphony*, showing a rich texture of different melodic types distributed among a chorus and the instruments of a large orchestra. Find within the excerpt the following melodic types, and list them by indicating the parts in which they occur and their measure numbers:

   a. The "tune" which is the principal melody. (Include duplicating parts.) _____

   _____

   b. Parts that form a chordal texture with the principal melody but that do not have

   any particular prominence. _____

   c. An "interior accompaniment." _____

   d. A countermelody. _____

e. A collateral part. _____

f. A significant repeated-note figure. _____

g. Figurational activity. _____

Beethoven, *Symphony No. 9*, IV

97

2. The three melodic excerpts that follow are for practice with the procedure discussed in your main text (p. 101 ff.; see Example 7–27). Space has been provided for you to complete the following steps of this procedure:

   a. Renotate the melody, with repeated tones merged into single tones.
   b. Rewrite the melody again, deleting all the tones of lesser durational or metrical importance that act as stepwise connectors to the tones of greater importance. Tones connected by neighbor notes may be subsumed into single tones.
   c. In a third renotation, remove barlines, rests, and other durational signs. Notate the principal tones of each measure with white noteheads, with descending stems beamed together, thus:

Connect like pitches with broken beams attached to ascending stems: _etc._

Notate tones of secondary importance (arpeggiative notes, passing tones, etc.) with unstemmed black noteheads:

   d. Renotate again, placing the arpeggiations on the same stems with their principals.
   e. Renotate once more, leaving only the principals.

   It should be kept in mind that not all of these steps will apply to every melody. Some melodies can be reduced in fewer steps; others may not have obvious applications of the steps.

Smetana, *The Moldau*

a.

b.

c.

d.

e.

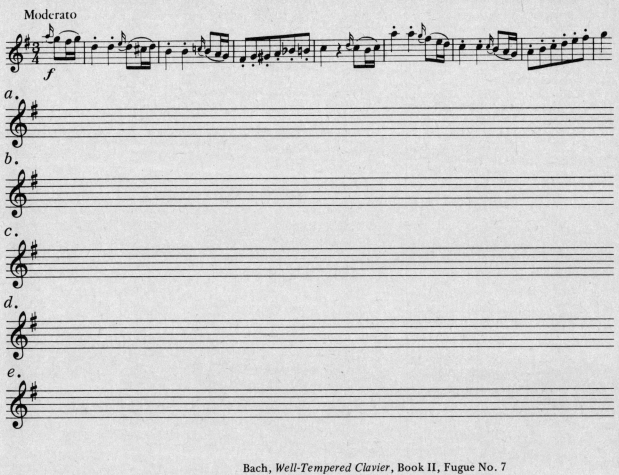

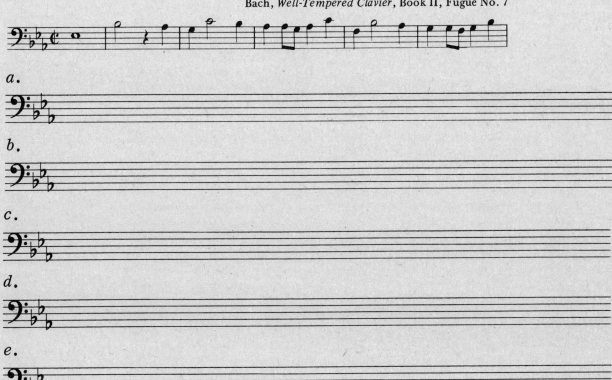

Bach, *Well-Tempered Clavier*, Book II, Fugue No. 7

3. For additional melodic material to study, you may search among the following kinds of music (though this is hardly an exhaustive list of genres that will afford worthy melodies):

       a. art songs (German, *Lieder*; French, *mélodies*) by Schubert, Schumann, Wolf, and many others;

       b. operatic solos and choruses;

       c. vocal works with obbligato instrumental solos (some fine examples can be found in the arias of Bach's cantatas, Mozart's operas, Weber's *Der Freischütz*);

       d. collections of folk tunes, hymns, patriotic songs, etc.;

       e. instrumental music having prominent parts for melody instruments.

Here are some suggestions for what you should consider in analyzing what you find (restudy also pp. 114–15 of the main text):

    a. Observations regarding the general shape and contour:
       1. What are the significant high and low tones of the melody?
       2. What is its predominant register?
       3. Draw a line approximating the overall contour and shape of the melody.

    b. Observations regarding the parts of the melody:
       1. How many measures in all? How many sections?
       2. Locate all cadences and identify them (see also Chapter 12).
       3. Determine individual phrase lengths; count the total number of phrases.
       4. Identify all subsections of phrases, and all motives.

    c. Observations regarding the relation of the parts of the melody to each other and to the whole, and the relation of the melody to the entire piece:
       1. Trace all motives through the entire melody, determining types of transformations and number of repetitions.
       2. Find out what use is made of figuration, such as extending or connecting various parts of the phrase.
       3. Compare subsequent phrases to the first phrase of each section or the first phrase of the entire piece. Note similarities and differences in length, character, function, etc.
       4. Determine the roles of repetition, variation, and contrast between the first and subsequent phrases.

Section C (Programmed Series) and Section D (Composition Activities) are not included in this unit.

SECTION E

Self Test

1. The word _____ describes any group of tones meant to be heard as a succession.

2. A succession of tones, deliberately contrasted with a principal melody, both rhythmically and contrapuntally, is called a _____ .

3. A collateral part parallels, or follows the line of, a principal melody, most usually in intervals of _____ or _____ .

4. A short melody, usually in the bass, that repeats over and over again is called _____ .

5. A succession of tones in a repeated pattern that projects harmony more than melody is called a _____ .

6. A _____ is a short thematic unit, melodic or rhythmic or both, which is subject to repetition and transformation.

7. A perceived unit of musical thought which measures the beginning and ending of a melodic unit is called a _____ .

8. The terms _____ and _____ indicate phrases in natural pairs, in which the second phrase seems to complement or answer the first.

9. _____ is the adding of decorative tones to a subsequent appearance of a melodic unit in such a way that its original form or profile can still be discerned.

Nonharmonic Tones

SECTION A

Words and Abbreviations to Know

Define and memorize:

nonharmonic
contrapuntal
polyphonic
auxiliary tone, auxiliary (aux.)
neighbor note, neighbor (N)
incomplete neighbor note (IN)
passing tone (p.t., +)
anticipation (ant.)
appoggiatura (app.)

suspension (S)
escape tone (E)
reaching tone (R)
échappée
cambiata
ornamental resolution
free tone
pedal, pedal point

Contrast:

melodic dissonance/harmonic dissonance
passing tone/neighbor note
suspension/prepared appoggiatura
escape tone/reaching tone

SECTION B

Technical Exercises

1. The following two-voice fragments contain various types of nonharmonic tones. Determine the type and the precise location of these nonharmonic tones, indicating them with the appropriate symbols or abbreviations (p.t., N, S, etc.). In some instances the complete chord is not present, but the chord symbols below each example will guide you.

F: VI   IV   C: V   A: VI   V   a: V   II⁶   B♭: V⁶   VI⁶

c: VI   I   G: I   V⁶₄   C: V_____   A: V_____

A: II⁶ V   d: I_____   C: V_____   F: I_____

F: I   II   I   E♭: I   II⁶   C: IV_____   A: V⁷_____

2. Work out two versions of the given figured bass line. In the first version include a number of appoggiature; in the second, suspensions and anticipations. Use no other nonharmonic tones except passing tones. All nonharmonic tones employed are to move in eighth-note values, except in the last measure, where they may move in quarter-note values.

(adapted from Schumann)

3. The following long figured bass is to be realized in four parts, the upper parts moving mostly in eighth-note and sixteenth-note values, freely incorporating nonharmonic tones of all types. In working out the exercise, you should note that the bass melody falls into four-bar semiphrases, some of which are similar; plan your soprano melody accordingly. (A rest in the bass, needless to say, does not have to be matched by rests in the upper parts.)

(adapted from Verdi, *La Traviata*)

4. Work out two versions of the figured bass given below, as follows:

   a. In two parts, the added part moving entirely in eighth notes, and incorporating passing tones, neighbor notes, and appoggiature;

   b. In four parts, incorporating at least one suspension, one anticipation, one escape tone, and one reaching tone (other nonharmonic tones may also be used if you wish).

5. In each of the three following excerpts, label all nonharmonic tones and write in the simple chord forms in the blank staff underneath.

William Mason, *Dance Antique*, Op. 38

Beethoven, *Sonata*, Op. 14, No. 1, II

Section C, Programmed Series, is not included in this unit.

SECTION D

Composition Activities

1. A chordal accompaniment is given below. Write three original melodies to go with it. In the first version, use no nonharmonic tones except passing tones. In the second version, use suspensions with ornamental resolutions, plus passing tones and neighbor notes, as you wish. In the third version, use nonharmonic tones of any type.

(adapted from Schumann)

2. An eight-measure excerpt by Schumann is given below. Use it as a theme on which to write four or five variations. You may keep most of Schumann's piano texture and pattern, mainly varying the upper line; or you may change the texture entirely, keeping only the harmonic structure. (For the former, you will find it helpful to review the end of Chapter 7 of your main text, pp. 99–105; for the latter, you should prepare by reading ahead in the text, at the end of Chapter 9, pp. 146–48.)

Schumann, *Album for the Young*, Op. 68: No. 20, *Rustic Song*

*This is a passing chord, V of II; you may use it or omit it, as you wish.

SECTION E
Self Test

1. The term *melodic dissonance* describes dissonance in a musical texture resulting from the inclusion of _____ tones.

2. Do nonharmonic tones, nonchord tones, and nontriadic tones all represent essentially the same phenomenon? _____

3. A minimum of two voices sounding simultaneously is needed to produce melodic dissonance: true or false? _____

4. Our recognition of nonharmonic tones suggests that dissonance in tonal music is rigidly controlled, and that in this control _____ motion plays an important part.
conjunct / disjunct

5. Any dissonance in tonal music must have a possible stepwise resolution to a

_____ .

6. Melodic motion can both generate and _____ dissonance.

7. The neighbor note (auxiliary) and the passing tone involve only _____ motion.

8. The motion to and from a neighbor note is always stepwise and in the _____ direction.

9. The neighbor note is always on a _____ beat or part of the beat.

10. A tone that in all respects is like a neighbor note, but that falls on a strong beat, is called _____ .

11. The _____ consists of the advance sounding of a tone as a sort of upbeat.

12. The nonharmonic tone that fills a melodic skip by means of stepwise motion in the same direction is called a _____ .

13. Passing tones are always _____ . Otherwise, they would be called appoggiature.

14. What is a suspension? _____

_____

15. A suspended tone that is not tied, but is reattacked on the strong beat, is called an _____ , though it is a particular type in that it is prepared.

16. The nonharmonic tone usually involving a step-skip motion and which is usually metrically weak is called _____ .

17. A leap up or down, followed by stepwise motion in the opposite direction is called _____ .

18. *Échappée* and *cambiata* are older names for _____ and _____ respectively.

The Harmonic Structure of the Phrase

Words to Know

Define and memorize:

cadence
half cadence, semicadence
thesis
anacrusis
harmonic sequence

Contrast:

masculine ending/feminine ending
half cadence/authentic cadence

Technical Exercises

1. Given below are some guidelines for analysis of the harmonic structure of a phrase, followed by three excerpts for you to analyze. The guidelines are intended to assist you in these exercises, but you should also refer to them, if you need to, when analyzing any music from this viewpoint. (Special attention might be paid to music that you are studying for performance.)

Guidelines for Analysis of the Harmonic Structure of a Phrase

1. What is the number of measures included in the phrase?
2. Determine the real-time duration (i.e., in seconds) of a typical phrase in the particular piece. (If the piece has a metronome marking this can easily be computed; if it does not, measure it directly with a stop-watch, choosing a tempo that is appropriate.)
3. What is the average number of different harmonies per phrase?

4. What types of chords are used, and with what frequency? Are tonal-degree triads used principally? Are modal-degree triads used at all?

5. Consider the relative use of root position and first inversion.

6. What chord is used for the beginning of the phrase? Does this vary from phrase to phrase?

7. Identify the chords used at the cadence.

8. What bearing does the melodic structure of the phrase have on the harmonic structure? Does the melodic rhythm match the harmonic rhythm? Do the harmonic changes coincide with the motivic details of the melody?

9. Do the successive phrases generally tend to relate to each other in terms of balanced pairs, that is, as antecedent and consequent? If not, what is the usual relationship between successive phrases?

10. Are the endings of the phrases usually masculine or feminine?

11. Note any similarities in the root progressions from phrase to phrase or from semiphrase to semiphrase. Do rhythmic or melodic motives appear? Is harmonic sequence used?

12. Consider the distribution of chord types generally: is a balance between unity and variety actually achieved? If not, what type of organizational plan prevails?

Mendelssohn, *Song Without Words*, Op. 102: No. 3

Bach, Chorale No. 173, *O Herzensangst, O Bangigkeit und Zagen*

Liszt, *Apparition No. 2*

Note: From this point on, in all exercises in realization of a figured bass or harmonization of an unfigured bass, you should assume that free motion of the upper parts is permitted unless the directions state otherwise; in other words, the note-against-note restriction no longer holds automatically. "Free motion" will of course include the use of nonharmonic tones, whether or not they are indicated.

110

2. Work out the figured basses given below in three or four parts, and label keys and chords. After completing each one, study it from the standpoint of the guidelines given in No. 1 above; then summarize your findings in a short paragraph or in outline form, using appropriate terminology.

(adapted from Bach, *Well-Tempered Clavier*, Book II: Prelude No. 19)

(adapted from Beethoven, *Sonata*, Op. 28, III ("Pastorale"))

Scherzo: Allegro vivace

Sections C (Programmed Series) and D (Composition Activities) are not included in this unit.

SECTION E

Self Test

1. The number of measures in a phrase will usually be _____ .

2. In most phrases there will probably be _____ changes of harmony than there are beats in the phrase.
   more / fewer

3. Eight measures, in a moderate tempo, very probably will constitute a relatively
   _____ phrase.
   long / short

4. *Thesis* is another word for _____ , while *anacrusis* refers to the _____ .

5. The _____ always signals the phrase ending, just as the beginning of a phrase can be determined by locating the _____ of the previous phrase.

6. Cadential types have been compared to punctuation marks, with the _____ cadence being in effect like the comma, and the _____ cadence being comparable to the full stop, or period.

7. If the final chord is on a strong beat the ending is called _____ ; otherwise it is called a _____ ending.

8. Successive repetitions of a harmonic progression on other pitch levels, or in other keys, is called a _____ .

9. Harmonic _____ is a concept that relates both to the distribution of chords in the phrase and to the frequency of chord changes.

Harmonization of a Given Part

Sections A (Words to Know), C (Programmed Series), D (Composition Activities), and
E (Self Test) are not included in this unit.

SECTION B

Technical Exercises

1. Below are several three-note melodic fragments in various keys. Each one is to be
harmonized note against note in several different ways (five different ways for those
in major, three for those in minor). Use only triads in root position or first inversion.
Write your harmonizations in stemless white notes, like the given fragments. When
you have completed the exercise, play each harmonization several times at the piano,
experimenting with different rhythmic and metric values, such as:

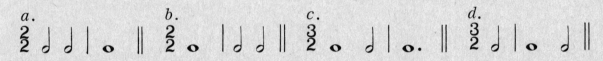

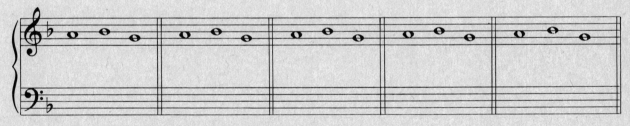

F:

A:

G:

f:

a:

114

2. The following three-note soprano fragments are given with several alternative basses, each having a gap where the second note should be. The given bass notes do not specify whether a root-position or first-inversion triad should be used. Determine the most suitable harmonization for each middle note, and fill in the missing alto and tenor parts for the other chords according to what will sound best. **Label** each chord.

D:

c♯:

B♭:

C:

eb:

3. Write four different harmonizations (not necessarily note against note) of the following familiar phrase. Study the melody carefully before proceeding to the actual harmonizations.

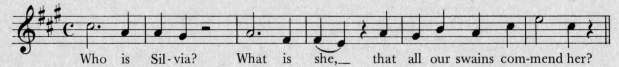

Schubert, *To Sylvia* (text originally from Shakespeare, *The Two Gentlemen of Verona*)

Who is Sil-via? What is she,— that all our swains com-mend her?

a.

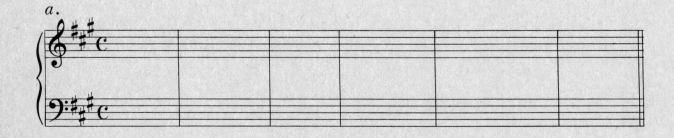

b.

c.

d.

4. Harmonize the following phrases drawn from chorale melodies:

Schwing' dich auf zu deinem Gott

Allein Gott in der Höh' sei Ehr

Nun sich der Tag geendet hat

Gott der Vater, wohn' uns bei

Herr, ich habe missgehandelt

Dank sei Gott in der Höhe

Jesu, der du meine Seele

O Lamm Gottes unschuldig

Schmücke dich, o liebe Seele

Hast du denn, Jesu, dein Angesicht gänzlich verborgen

UNIT ELEVEN
The Six-Four Chord

SECTION A
Words to Know

Define and memorize:

cadential six-four chord   arpeggiating six-four chord
appoggiatura six-four chord   auxiliary six-four chord
passing six-four chord

SECTION B
Technical Exercises

1. The following figured-bass formulae illustrate the characteristic uses of the six-four chord. Work each one out in four parts, note against note, and in a variety of chord spacings, using the regular voice leading described in Chapter 11 of the main text. Label all chords with appropriate roman and arabic numerals. Your solutions will provide a good reference source for later restudy of the six-four chord as it is usually employed.

a. Cadential six-four

b. Auxiliary six-four

c. Passing six-four

2. Various uses of the six-four chord are represented in the following figured basses derived from the literature. As you work these out in four parts, indicate the function of each six-four chord by writing "cadential," "passing," etc., as the case may be.

Schubert, *Valses sentimentales*, Op. 50 (freely adapted)

Beethoven, *Trio*, Op. 97 ("Archduke"), IV (freely adapted)

Schubert, *Graz Waltzes*, Op. 91a (adapted)

Mozart, *Rondo*, K. 485 (adapted)

Programmed Series

---

1. In what key is the following excerpt? _____

Beethoven, *Piano Concerto No. 1*, Op. 15, I

Allegro con brio

(*pp*)

---

2. Label the chords in the last two measures of the excerpt above.

---

3. The lowest notes in the last two measures of this excerpt are no more than an octave

duplication of the _____ voice in a basic four-part structure. Cross out these duplicated notes.

---

4. What factor is doubled in the six-four chord? _____

---

5. In the blank staves given below, using stemless black notes, write out the six-four chord found in the excerpt above in four parts, together with the chord that precedes it and the chord that follows it, and show the voice leading by means of straight lines connecting the successive tones.

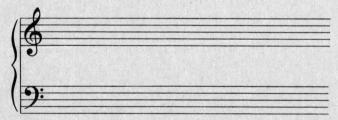

---

6. Your results should look like the following:

7. The motion of the individual moving voices is _____ .

conjunct / disjunct

8. The use of the six-four above is called the _____ six-four. How does it differ from a cadential six-four? _____

9. Without regard to the actual barline, but relative only to the two tonic chords that surround it, is this six-four chord metrically strong or weak? _____

10. Taking into consideration its placement within the measure, is the six-four chord relatively strong or weak metrically? _____

11. In what key is the following excerpt? _____

Mozart, *Violin Sonata*, K. 301, I

Allegro con spirito

12. Label the chords in the excerpt above.

13. By deleting duplicating voices, construct an SATB reduction of the I$^6_4$ chord and the V^7 that follows it, using whole and half notes, on two staves only.

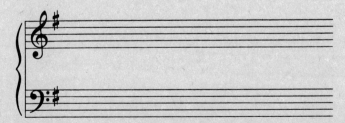

14. The reduction above is identical to the ordinary formulation of the _____ six-four and its resolution.

15. Does Mozart's original version of this formula place the six-four on a strong or weak beat of the measure? _____ Is this a characteristic usage for this type of six-four? _____

16. The _____ of the triad is doubled in this six-four chord.

17. The motion of the other factors in the resolution of the six-four is by _____ in a _____ direction.

18. What is the key of the following excerpt? _____

Clementi, *Sonatina*, Op. 36, No. 4, III

19. The excerpt above contains two different six-four chords. The first that appears is in measure _____ on beat _____ . The second is in measure _____ on beat _____ .

20. The first six-four is on a _____ beat and is an example of a _____ six-four. The second is on a weak beat and is an example of a _____ six-four.

21. In what way is the resolution of the six-four in the first measure not typical?

_____

_____

Section D (Composition Activities) is not included in this unit.

Self Test

1. When a triad is in the _____ inversion it is called a six-four chord.

2. The _____ of the chord is in the bass when the triad is in the six-four position.

3. The dissonant interval that exists when a major or minor triad is in the six-four position is the _____ .

4. The six-four chord is thought of generally as _____ chord.

a stable / an unstable

5. The chord factor that is most usually doubled in the six-four is the _____ .

6. A strong tonic six-four, usually unprepared, and resolving to a dominant chord as a double appoggiatura, is called a _____ six-four.

7. The distinguishing characteristics of the cadential six-four are:
   a. _____ b. _____ and
   c. _____

8. The motion of the voices in the resolution of the cadential tonic six-four to the dominant is _____ by _____ .

9. The cadential six-four _____ often placed immediately after the barline.

is / is not

10. A tonic six-four to dominant progression, in a strong-weak relationship within the phrase rather than at the end, is called the _____ six-four.

11. Triads other than the tonic _____ be used as appoggiatura six-four chords.

may / may not

12. The distinguishing characteristics of the passing six-four are:
    a. _____ b. _____ and
    c. _____

13. The six-four in which two factors function as neighbor notes is the _____ six-four chord.

14. The auxiliary six-four chord is usually on a _____ beat.

15. Triads built on the _____ degrees of the scale are more often found in the six-four position than are those built on _____ degrees.

16. The distinguishing characteristics of the auxiliary six-four are:

a. _____ b. _____ and

c. _____ .

17. The passing six-four chord gets its name from the motion of the _____ .

18. A typical chord progression involving the passing six-four chord could be: _____
_____ .

_____

UNIT TWELVE
Cadences

SECTION A
Words to Know

Define and memorize:

authentic cadence   deceptive cadence
half cadence   Phrygian cadence

Contrast:

perfect cadence/imperfect cadence

SECTION B
Technical Exercises

In addition to emphasizing cadences, the following figured basses derived from the literature will provide useful practice in three- and four-part writing, incorporating almost all of the principles brought forth in earlier units.

Label all cadences throughout this section, as well as all chords and inversions. Also identify all six-four usages by type.

Alternate and additional versions of these exercises may be worked out if you wish, each beginning with a different spacing.

Beethoven, *Sonata*, Op. 31, No. 2 ("Tempest"), I

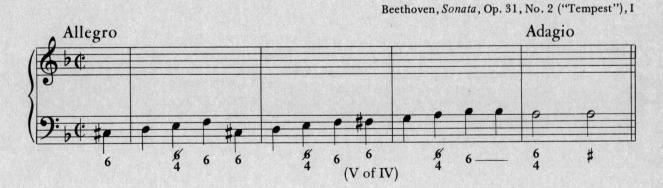

129

Allegro

Section C (Programmed Series) is not included in this unit.

SECTION D

Composition Activities

Continue the given piano fragment in four different ways, ending each phrase with the cadence indicated. The intervening measures should utilize various different harmonic progressions, with one harmony change per measure sufficing in most cases.

a.

(authentic cadence)

b.

(half cadence)

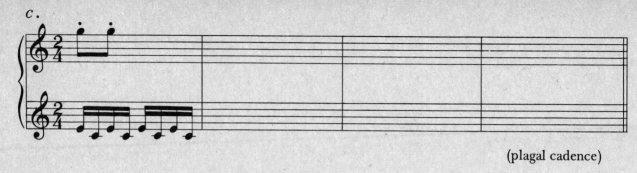

c.

(plagal cadence)

d.

(deceptive cadence,
using VI or IV⁶)

SECTION E
Self Test

1. Harmonic formulae used for phrase endings which "mark the breathing places in music, establish the tonality, and render coherent the formal structure" are called

   _____ .

2. The authentic cadence comprises the progression _____ to _____ .

3. The chord commonly preceding the authentic cadential formula will often be either

   _____ or _____ .

4. The authentic cadential formula _____ be preceded by I_4^6.
   _{may / may not}

5. The progression $IV–I_4^6–V–I$, appearing at a final cadence, will be very _____
   in terms of its finality.   strong / weak

6. The most conclusive arrangement of the authentic cadence, with tonic and dominant chords in root position and the tonic note in the soprano at the end, is called a

   _____ cadence.

7. All forms of the authentic cadence other than that just described in No. 6 above are

   termed _____ cadences, meaning that they are less _____ .

8. When the final chord of a cadential harmonic formula is a dominant, then the cadence is called a _____ cadence.

9. The plagal cadence "is most often used after an authentic cadence, as a sort of added close to a movement," and consists of the harmonic progression _____ to _____ .

10. The minor form of subdominant harmony _____ used in the plagal
    is occasionally / is never
    cadence at the end of a movement in the major mode.

11. The _____ cadence "is similar to the authentic except that some other chord is substituted for the final tonic."

12. The chord most frequently substituted for the tonic in the cadence described in No. 11 above is the _____ chord.

13. A IV^6—V final cadence in the minor mode, appearing at the end of a slow movement or slow introduction, is called a _____ cadence.

Harmonic Rhythm

SECTION A
Words to Know

Define and memorize:

static harmony   melodic rhythm
harmonic rhythm   rhythmic texture
nonharmonic chords   pulse

Contrast:

meter/rhythm/pulse

SECTION B
Technical Exercises

1. Realize the derived figured basses given below. For each bass, provide a complete root analysis and answer the following questions in the spaces provided:

   a. Does the harmonic rhythm reflect at least in a general way the meter of the composition?

   b. Are the durations of the separate chords approximately the same most of the time, or are they generally different for each chord or each group of chords?

   c. Is each new chord introduced on a strong beat of the measure most of the time? If not, what proportion of the total number of chords are introduced on strong beats?

   d. Would you characterize the rate of change of chords as quite slow, rather slow, somewhat fast, or quite fast?

   e. Prepare an inventory of the intervals between the roots of all progressions.

   f. Is the general effect of the overall harmonic rhythm one of restlessness, one of breadth and relaxation, or something best described in other terms?

   g. Characterize the harmonic rhythm and the changes in dynamics as abrupt or gradual and compare.

   h. Is there any part with a static harmonic layer deriving from one or more pedal points? If so, state precisely where it is.

i. Are there any nonharmonic chords? If so, state precisely where and what kind they are. Whatever your answer, explain your reasons for it.

Corelli, *Gigue* (adapted)

a. _____

b. _____

c. _____

d. _____

e. _____

f. _____

g. _____

h. _____

i. _____

Bach, Chorale No. 153, *Alle Menschen müssen sterben*

a. _____

b. _____

c. _____

d. _____

e. _____

f. _____

g. _____

h. _____

i. _____

Mozart, *Piano Concerto*, K. 456, I (adapted)

Allegro vivace

a. _____

b. _____

c. _____

d. _____

e. _____

f. _____

g. _____

h. _____

i. _____

136

Allegro ma non troppo

a. _____

b. _____

c. _____

d. _____

e. _____

f. _____

g. _____

h. _____

i. _____

Wagner, *Lohengrin*, Act II, scene 4: Elsa's Procession

a. _____

b. _____

c. _____

d. _____

e. _____

f. _____

g. _____

h. _____

i. _____

2. In these exercises, an extra staff has been provided beneath each musical excerpt so that you can write down the close-position chord that represents the essential harmony at each point of change. When you have completed that task, answer the same series of questions as in No. 1 above.

Beethoven, *Sonata*, Op. 10, No. 1, II

a. _____

b. _____

c. _____

d. _____

e. _____

f. _____

g. _____

h. _____

i. _____

Schumann, *Phantasiestücke*, Op. 12: No. 8, *Ende vom Lied*

Etwas lebhaft

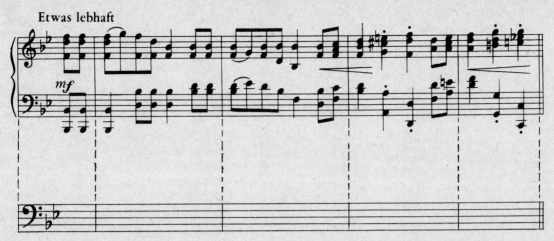

a. _____
b. _____
c. _____
d. _____
e. _____
f. _____
g. _____
h. _____
i. _____

Brahms, *Rhapsody*, Op. 79, No. 2

Molto passionato, ma non troppo allegro

a. _____

b. _____

c. _____

d. _____

e. _____

f. _____

g. _____

h. _____

i. _____

Sections C (Programmed Series) and D (Composition Activities) are not provided for this Unit.

Self Test

1. Frequency of _____ change and the _____ quality of the change are the two main features of harmonic rhythm.

2. Is the harmonic rhythm affected when a chord merely changes position, whether or not the bass is repeated? _____

3. Any assessment of the harmonic rhythm of a composition _____ include a
   should / need not
   consideration of the dynamics of the music.

4. Some chords that primarily for rhythmic reasons do not attain the status of independent harmonies are called _____ chords.

5. Harmonic rhythm _____ correspond to the meter.
   must always / need not

6. In common time, when a chord is introduced on the first or third beat it is said to have relative _____ .

7. When the harmonic changes are few and far between, the harmonic rhythm is said to be _____ .

8. Very frequent changes of harmony will create a feeling of _____ .

9. The presence of a pedal point tends to create a _____ harmonic layer in the music.

Modulation

SECTION A

Words to Know

Define and memorize:

static tonality	enharmonic modulation	tonicize, tonicization
modulation	intermediate modulation	related keys
modulatory process	modulation chain	parallel scales
pivot chord	abrupt modulation	shift

Contrast:

tonicization/intermediate modulation
modulation/interchange of mode
enharmonic change/abrupt modulation

SECTION B

Technical Exercises

1. On the staff provided, write the triads that would be suitable for use as pivot chords in a modulation between the two keys designated. Include only chords that are actual triadic members of the keys involved, without invoking secondary dominants, chords from the opposite mode, etc. Label each chord with roman numerals indicating root function in each key.

Example

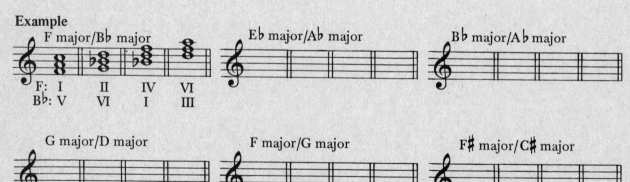

2. The following will include minor scales. In working out the process of modulation involving keys in the minor mode, you should consider all the triads built on the degrees of the harmonic minor scale, together with the variants available from the melodic forms:

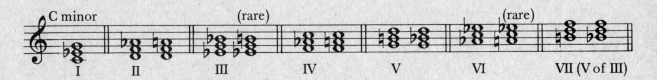

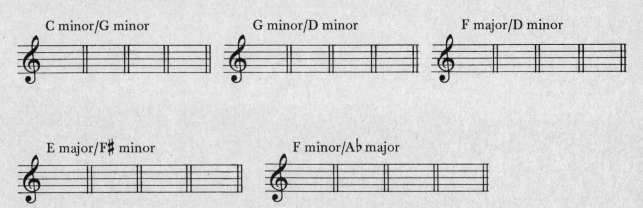

With these in mind, write the potential pivot chords in modulations between the following pairs of keys:

C minor/G minor   G minor/D minor   F major/D minor

E major/F♯ minor   F minor/A♭ major

3. Because of enharmonic relationships, certain keys may be closely related even though their notation causes them to appear distant from each other. For example, C-sharp major, seven sharps, and D-flat major, five flats, are really the same key. Give below all potential pivot chords, together with their enharmonic equivalents, between the designated pairs of keys. Label each chord with roman numerals indicating root function in each key.

Example

E♭ major/C♯ major   B major/G♭ major   G♭ major/C♯ major

E♭: II   IV
C♯: III   V

C♯ minor/A♭ major   F♯ major/E♭ minor

4. Occasionally a pivot is used that involves a change in mode in one of the keys. For example, in a modulation from D major to B-flat major, the minor IV of D might be used as the VI in B flat. Thus modal interchange provides additional possibilities for pivot chords between two keys. Below, write *only* those pivots that might be obtained from the opposite mode of the first key in each given pair.

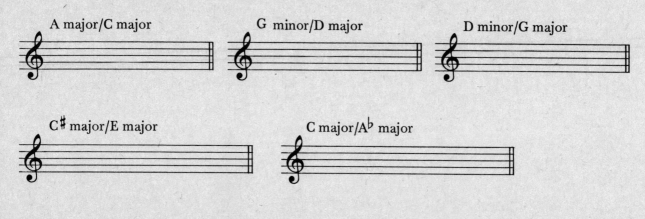

A major/C major   G minor/D major   D minor/G major

C♯ major/E major   C major/A♭ major

SECTION C

Analysis

In this section three complete pieces or movements are included for study of their tonal relationships. In your initial approach to these pieces, you may find it helpful to read through the following guidelines.

Guidelines for the Observation of Key Structure in Music

1. Observe the initial tonality of the composition. How long does the particular scale prevail?

    a. When do chromatic pitches significantly affect the harmony, suggesting that the state of tonality is in the process of change, or has changed?

    b. At what point are the tonal degrees of the initial key displaced by other tones, in terms of durational, metrical, and other stresses?

    c. Identify the new tonal degrees and the pitch collection or scale from which they are derived. (The point where these are stabilized will necessarily follow any passage where the sense of tonality is interrupted or suspended.)

2. Observe the new tonality. How long does the new scale prevail? (Refer back to 1a and 1b above, as necessary.)

    a. Is the change in the tonality state simply a tonicization? If so, which pitch is tonicized, and for how long?

    b. Is the change an intermediate modulation? What pitch is used as a temporary keynote? What relationship does it bear to the principal tonality, and how many measures are involved?

    c. Is the change part of a modulation chain? If it is, then determine the keynote of each successive tonality in the chain, along with durations (in terms of numbers of measures) of each.

    d. Is the change a single actual modulation? What is its duration, relative to the initial extent of the old key?

3. Repeat the procedures listed above, in whole or in part, as often as necessary until the end of the composition or movement is reached.

Beethoven, *Sonata*, Op. 49, No. 1, Rondo

146

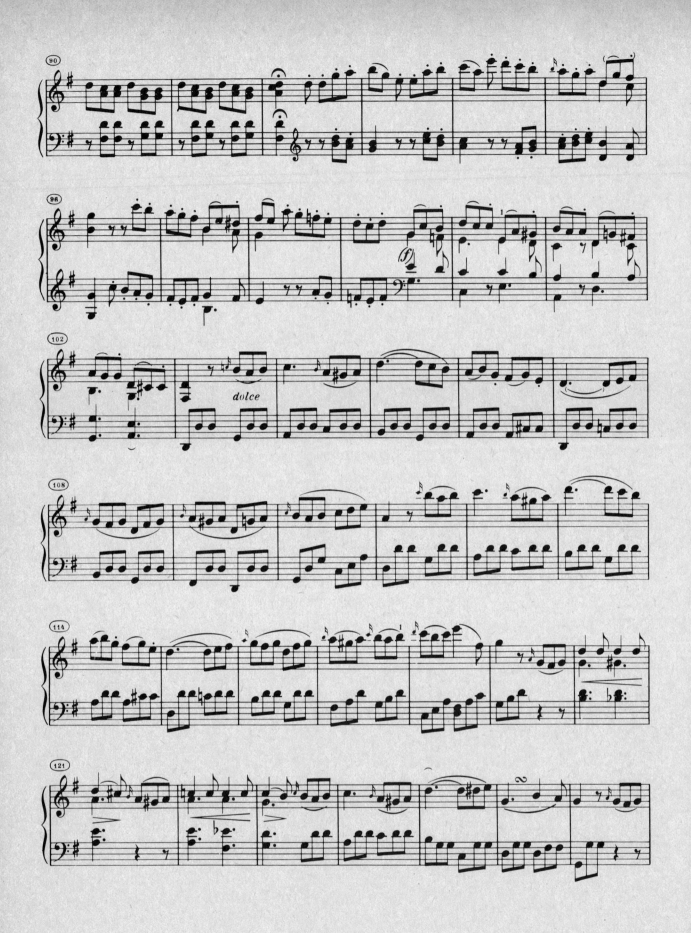

148

149

Bach, *French Suite No. 1*, Courante

Observations

Chopin, *Prelude*, Op. 28, No. 15 ("Raindrop")

Observations

Changes in the tonality of a composition often go hand in hand with other form-delineating changes, such as changes in texture or meter, the apparent beginning of a contrasting section, and so forth. Does the change of key in each of the pieces above contribute to the hearing of the composition in well-defined sections? In other words, does the change of key affect your perception of the form of the piece? Give reasons for your answer in each case.

a. Beethoven, Rondo:

_____
_____
_____
_____
_____

b. Bach, Courante:

_____
_____
_____
_____
_____

c. Chopin, Prelude:

_____
_____
_____
_____
_____

SECTION D

Composition Activities

1. Write an extended melody for solo clarinet, based upon your observations of the tonality in the Bach Courante given earlier in this unit. Your melody will have the same number of measures as the Bach original, will follow its key scheme exactly, and will have its same general formal characteristics, but in all other ways will be different. You should thus consider writing your composition with an entirely different meter and rhythmic character; supply your own tempo, phrasing, articulation, and dynamics with care. Keep the melody generally within the middle register of the instrument.

2. Using the Chopin Prelude given earlier in this unit as a model, write a duet for flutes, of not more than moderate difficulty. Use the same number of measures as the Chopin original and keep to the same scheme of tonality and other sectional characteristics (though for ease of performance you may begin your piece in D major instead of D-flat major). See to it that both flute parts are of approximately equal musical interest; do not write one subsidiary to the other.

3. As a more extensive project along the lines of Nos. 1 and 2 above, write a Rondo for violin and cello, based on the Beethoven Rondo provided earlier in this unit. Make sure that the instruments share the principal thematic material and the secondary accompanimental material more or less equally.

═══

SECTION E

Self Test

1. When a piece of music employs only notes drawn from a fixed diatonic collection of pitch-classes, it is said to be in a _____ state of tonality.

2. The key scheme, or pattern of keys, in a composition is one of the most significant ingredients of its _____ .

3. There are _____ stages in the mental process of effecting a modulation.

4. It _____ essential that the tonic chord appear for the establishment of a key.
   is / is not

5. A chord common to both keys which will be conveniently susceptible to the change of tonal viewpoint is a potential _____ in the modulatory process.

6. Between the keys of G major and D major there are _____ potential pivot chords available.

7. Between the keys of A major and C-sharp major there are _____ possible pivot chords.

8. In order to relate keys such as G-flat major and C-sharp major, it is necessary to bring into consideration the concept of _____ change or equivalence.

9. The pivot chord chosen is preferably not the _____ of the second key.

10. Establishment of the new key may be confirmed by the introduction of a _____ in that key.

11. Tonicization _____ a genuine modulation.
    constitutes / does not constitute

12. The tonal strength of a tonicization is in direct proportion to the musical _____ through which it extends.

13. When, after confirmation by cadence in the new key, the old key immediately returns, the modulation is called an _____ modulation.

14. Modulations can be only secondary tonal events in a piece beginning and ending in the same key. (True or false?) _____

15. When the modulation from the main key is not followed by an immediate return but by another modulation to a third key, the succession is called a _____ .

16. If two keys have a relatively large number of tones in common, these keys are said to be _____ keys.

17. F-sharp major and C-sharp major _____ closely related keys.
    are / are not

18. F major and B-flat major _____ closely related keys.
    are / are not

19. Parallel keys, such as B-flat major and B-flat minor, are considered _____
    only distantly related /
    _____ .
    practically identical

20. Modal interchange expands the scope of related tonalities available for modulation; most often, modulation involving modal interchange is brought about by borrowing elements of the _____ within the basic context of the _____ mode, rather than vice versa.

21. The use of a C-minor tonic triad by modal interchange in C major _____ afford a convenient pivot in relation to B-flat major.
    would / would not

22. A modulation that sounds sudden or tonally remote is called an _____ modulation.

23. When no real pivot is heard, the instance is best described in terms of _____ rather than modulation.

The Dominant Seventh Chord

Words to Know

Define and memorize:

tendency tones

dominant seventh

dominant six-five

dominant four-three

dominant four-two

third inversion

harmonic dissonance

passing chord

unprepared dissonance

regular resolution

irregular resolution

Contrast:

$$V^7/V^6_5/V^4_3/V^4_2$$

SECTION B

Technical Exercises

1. The following dissonant intervals are taken from V^7 chords in various keys and positions. Identify each key, name each interval, and show the interval of natural resolution. (Assume that the tonic triad of resolution will be major.)

Example

2. Not all of the following seventh chords are dominant sevenths. Locate those that are and circle them. Indicate the name of the keynote of the scale from which each dominant seventh is derived.

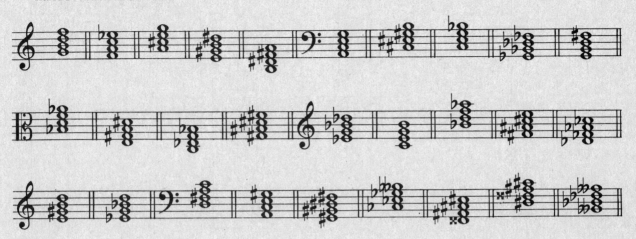

3. Circle the root of each chord below. (Some of the chords are not V⁷s; change them into V⁷s by adding appropriate accidentals.) Give the names of the key from which each V^7 is derived.

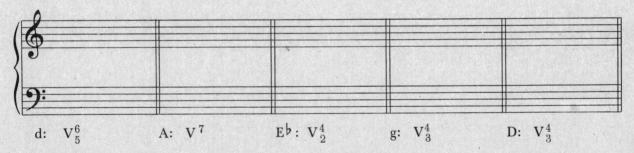

4. Write three different spacings in four parts for each of the following:

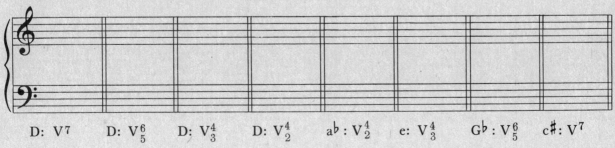

d: V^6_5 A: V^7 E♭: V^4_2 g: V^4_3 D: V^4_3

5. Construct the following dominant sevenths in the positions indicated, and provide regular resolutions for them with the usual voice leading.

D: V^7 D: V^6_5 D: V^4_3 D: V^4_2 a♭: V^4_2 e: V^4_3 G♭: V^6_5 c♯: V^7

6. Practice constructing dominant sevenths with omitted fifths, in the indicated positions. Resolve regularly.

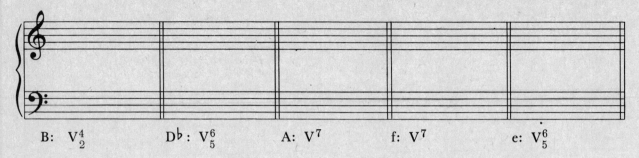

B: V_2^4 D♭: V_5^6 A: V^7 f: V^7 e: V_5^6

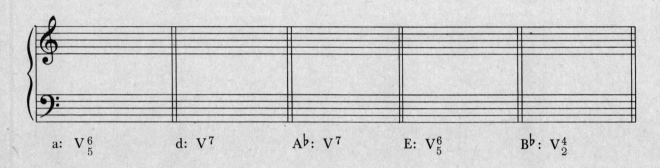

a: V_5^6 d: V^7 A♭: V^7 E: V_5^6 B♭: V_2^4

7. In each of the following, place the leading-tone of the V^7 in an inner voice; then write a smooth resolution to the tonic, moving the leading-tone down to the dominant note.

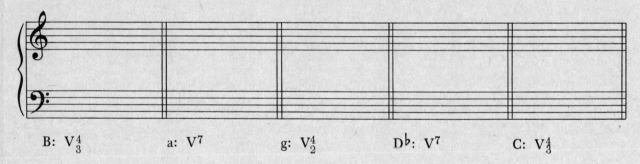

B: V_3^4 a: V^7 g: V_2^4 D♭: V^7 C: V_3^4

8. The following progressions are to be worked out so that the regular resolution of the dominant seventh to the tonic proceeds by irregular voice leading, resulting in the exceptional position or spacing indicated.

D: V_3^4 I^6 f: V_3^4 I^6 g: V^7 I^6 F: V^7 I^6 A: V_2^4 I^6 e♭: V_2^4 I^6 f♯: V_2^4 I G: V_2^4 I

9. Write two different versions of each of the following derived figured basses. Use non-harmonic tones freely.

Haydn, *Sonata No. 5*, I (adapted)

Rameau, *Le Forqueray* (adapted)

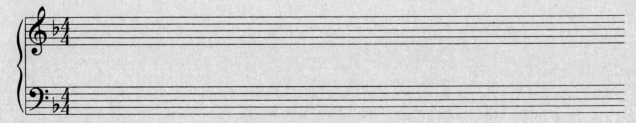

Programmed Series

1. The following excerpt is taken from the Courante of Bach's *French Suite No. 1*, included on page 150.

   Observe the dominant seventh chord found on the third and fourth quarters of the measure. The root of this chord is _____ .

2. Given below is the reduced form of this V⁷, together with its resolution.

   Is the chord of resolution complete or incomplete? _____ Discuss the voice leading of this progression.

   _____

   _____

   _____

3. Given below is the fifth measure of the same piece.

   What chord is tonicized in this passage? _____ Can you locate the V⁷ of F? Mark the place where it occurs. Observe all the nonharmonic tones carefully.

4. Here is a four-part reduction of the progression above.

Is this progression regular? Compare the reduction with the original. What kind of dissonance is the G in the alto of the chord of resolution? _____

_____

_____

_____

5. Discuss the voice leading in the above progression.

_____

_____

_____

_____

6. The final cadence of Bach's Courante is given below. Indicate all the V^7s in the excerpt.

7. Now examine the following reduction of the passage above, and compare it with the original excerpt.

8. Examine the second V^7 and analyze its seventh as a nonharmonic tone. What is interesting about its resolution? _____

_____

9. Find at least two more V^{7}s in the Bach Courante and list them here, stating precisely where they occur and how the seventh arises and is resolved. _____

_____

_____

_____

10. Examine the Beethoven Rondo given on page 145 at measures 147–50. Why is the seventh of the V^7 so prominent here? What eventually happens to it? _____

_____

_____

_____

11. Examine the Chopin Prelude given on page 151 at measure 60. In what key is the V^7 here? _____ In what position? _____ What factor is in the bass? _____ To what chord does the dominant seventh resolve? _____ Is this a regular resolution? _____ Explain why. _____

_____

12. The following additional illustrations of the importance of the dominant seventh chord are all drawn from the instrumental version of W. C. Handy's *The Memphis Blues,* or (*Mister Crump*).

Tempo di Blues

What is the apparent key of the excerpt above? _____ In what position is the dominant seventh on the first beat of the first full measure? _____ On the second beat? _____

13. What nonharmonic tones can you find in the first full measure? Are there in fact any at all? _____

14. B-flat major has been tonicized in the following excerpt.

Label both chords in relationship to this key.

15. The dominant seventh in the following excerpt suggests that either tonicization or modulation is involved. What temporary tonic is implied in this excerpt? _____
How do you account for the E? _____

16. Label all the chords in the following excerpt in relation to E-flat major. Also identify all nonharmonic tones.

17. In the final example, the principal key of B-flat major is reestablished. Identify the harmony on the downbeat of the first measure of this excerpt. _____ Identify the harmony in the second half of the same measure. _____ Where does

the latter harmony ultimately resolve? _____ What kind of
cadential formula is represented by this progression? _____

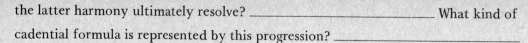

<hr />

Composition Activities

1. Write a four-part choral piece based on the harmonic scheme given below, using the
meter, tempo, and dynamic level indicated. Make the motion of the piece principally
homophonic, that is, with all parts moving for the most part together, and use only
note-values of a quarter note or longer. Equip your piece with a suitable text borrowed from a hymnbook or other anthology.

Chopin, *Prelude*, Op. 28, No. 7 (adapted)

2. Using the same harmonic scheme and bar pattern as in No. 1 above, write a short piano piece with a florid melody in the right hand. The left hand should contain no note-values faster than an eighth note, but the right hand may use sixteenths or even thirty-seconds.

SECTION E

Self Test

1. The dominant seventh chord always consists of a _____ third, a _____ fifth, and a _____ seventh, reckoned upward from the root of the chord.

2. Until the dominant seventh chord, the only dissonant chords we have studied are the diminished triads on _____ and _____ in the minor mode and on _____ in the major, and the augmented triad which may be found diatonically in the harmonic minor on the _____ degree.

3. The two dissonant intervals in the root-position dominant seventh chord are the
_____ and the _____ .

4. When inverted, these intervals become respectively the _____ and the
_____ .

5. Harmonically, the dissonant intervals are followed in their resolutions by
_____ intervals.

6. The diminished fifth is most often followed in resolution by a _____ or
_____ .

7. In resolution of the dominant seventh chord, the tendency of the seventh is to
_____ .

8. The leading-tone in the dominant seventh, when in the upper voice, will most usually
move _____ .

9. When in an inner voice in the dominant chord, the leading-tone may move up by step
to the tonic, or it may move _____ .

10. The augmented fourth on resolution will ordinarily expand to a _____ or
_____ .

11. Harmonically speaking, the regular resolution of the dominant seventh chord is to
the _____ chord.

12. When a complete dominant seventh chord in root position resolves regularly to the
tonic, the chord of resolution is incomplete, having three _____ and a
_____ .

13. In the resolution of V^7 to I, preference is _____ shown for the doubling of
usually / rarely
tonal degrees in the tonic chord, rather than modal degrees.

14. In an incomplete dominant seventh chord, the factor most likely to be omitted is
the _____ of the chord.

15. When the dominant seventh in root position progresses to the first-inversion tonic
triad, the seventh of the chord will move _____ so as to avoid doubling the
modal third degree in the tonic chord.

16. The last inversion of the dominant seventh chord is called the dominant _____
chord.

17. When an inverted dominant seventh chord resolves, the movement of the leading-tone
and the seventh _____ generally the same as though the dominant seventh chord
is / is not
were in root position.

18. The regular resolution of the dominant four-two is to _____ .

19. The dominant _____ is generally considered as being weaker rhythmically than the other inversions, and is often used as a passing chord between I and I^6; in this regard its function is identical with that of a dominant _____ with the seventh present.

UNIT SIXTEEN

Secondary Dominants

SECTION A

Words to Know

Define and memorize:

cross-relation
false relation
secondary dominant function
secondary tonic

chromatic alteration
chromatic tendency
"barber-shop" progression
V of . . .*

* In this Workbook and in your main text the preferred abbreviation is "V of V," not "V/V"; "V of VI," not "V/VI"; and so forth. The latter formulation, which is commonly used in other textbooks and by many teachers, is discouraged here because we will have another important use for the diagonal slash in our analytical symbols. That use is simply to indicate the presence of a pedal point or appoggiatura chord; for instance, "V/I," which is read as "five over one," will ordinarily denote a dominant chord surmounting a tonic bass. See Examples 8–18, 24–16, 24–20, 24–28, etc., in your main text.

SECTION B

Technical Exercises

1. Add a minor seventh above each note.

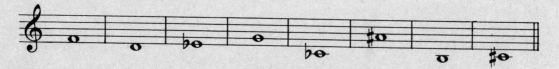

2. The answers to No. 1 above are provided below. Check your own answers and make any necessary corrections. Now add a diminished fifth below each upper tone, or, reckoning another way, add a major third above each lower tone.

3. Your answers should look like what appears below. Make any corrections that may be necessary. Now add to each chord a fourth tone so as to form a major triad with the bottom two tones.

4. The correct answers are provided below. Underneath each chord, name the keynote that is implied by the label V^7 of V being affixed to each chord.

Now, consider each chord to be V^7 of II of a key and name its keynote.

5. The pitches G, B, D, and F sounding together constitute the dominant seventh chord of C major and minor. It is also a potential secondary dominant in a number of keys, for instance, V^7 of IV in G major. What kind of secondary dominant is it with respect to each of the following keys?

A minor = _____   F major = _____

B-flat major = _____   E minor = _____

F minor = _____   G minor = _____

B-flat minor = _____   E-flat major = _____

A-flat major = _____

6. Label the chord D, F sharp, A, C as a secondary dominant with respect to each of the following keys:

F minor = _____ C minor = _____ D minor = _____

7. The chord E, G sharp, B, D, interpreted as a secondary dominant, would be labeled in the following keys as:

D minor = _____ C major = _____ G major = _____

F-sharp minor = _____

8. Label each of the following chords in relationship to the indicated keys.

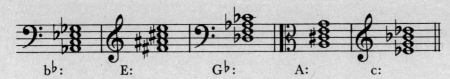

9. Write regular resolutions for the following secondary dominants. Label all chords and inversions.

Bb: Bb: Bb: Bb: Bb:

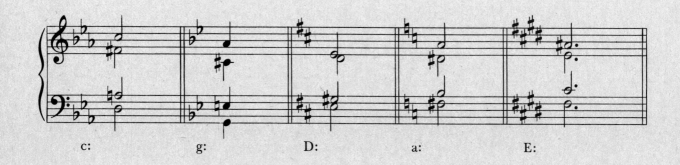

c: g: D: a: E:

10. Realize the following derived figured basses. Insofar as possible, resolve all dominant seventh chords and secondary dominants with the voice leading appropriate for resolutions of these chords. Provide a thorough root analysis.

Schubert, *Waltz*, Op. 18, No. 2 (adapted)

SECTION C

Analysis

A complete score of Chopin's *Mazurka*, Op. 33, No. 3, follows. Provide a detailed harmonic analysis, paying particular attention to dominant seventh chords and secondary dominants. Ascertain whether or not their resolutions are regular, and observe all details of their voice leading. In the blank staff provided below each line of music, write close-position chords representing the harmony above.

SECTION D

Composition Activities

1. Write a stormy passage for piano solo in moderate tempo, between eight and twelve measures long, using the harmonic scheme outlined below. The passage will end on a half cadence in F major. (You may wish to refer to the main text, pages 257–58.)

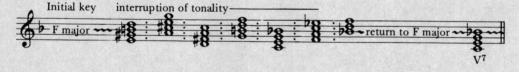

2. Using the harmonic scheme of Tchaikovsky's *Morning Prayer* found on page 173, choose your own meter and tempo and write a composition for piano, or, if you wish, for three or four instruments of any type available to your class, provided that the players can perform all the notes called for.

Section E (Self Test) is not provided for this unit.

Irregular Resolutions

Sections A (Words to Know), C (Programmed Series), and D (Composition Activities) are not provided for this unit.

SECTION B

Technical Exercises

Construct in four parts the following formulae involving irregular resolutions of the dominant seventh chord and of various secondary dominants.

Self Test

1. The resolution of the dominant seventh chord to any chord other than the
   _____ is considered to be an irregular resolution.

2. The irregular resolution having the same root motion as the ordinary exception to
   Rule of Thumb 2 in Chapter 3 (page 25 of the main text) is V^7 proceeding to _____ .

3. The irregular resolution of V^7 to V^7 of IV is hardly different from the _____
   resolution.

4. When two seventh chords appear in succession in root position, one of them will be
   _____ .

5. In what way are II and V of V functionally similar?

6. The II triad makes a _____ resolution for V^7.
   <u>strong / weak</u>

7. The resolution of V^7 to V of VI is _____ common.
   <u>fairly / not at all</u>

8. Perhaps the most common irregular resolution of V^7 is to _____ .

9. The type of resolution just referred to in No. 8 is very common in _____
   cadences.

10. The root movement of this resolution is by _____ .

11. When a secondary dominant resolves regularly, the root motion is upward by
    _____ or downward by _____ .

12. The commonest irregular resolution of a secondary dominant involves root movement
    that is _____ .

13. The kind of root movement just described in No. 12 is exactly comparable to that
    found in the irregular resolution of V^7 to _____ .

14. In its commonest irregular resolution, V^7 of III will proceed to _____ , the bass
    moving _____ to the _____ .

Problems in Harmonic Analysis

SECTION A

Words to Know

unitonal
dual-function chords
foreground
middleground
background
prolongation

Sections B (Technical Exercises), C (Programmed Series), D (Composition Activities), and E (Self Test) are not provided with this unit, just as regular exercises are not included in Chapter 18 of your main text. Instead, as in the main text, a project is provided here which can be kept small or expanded markedly, as time permits.

PROJECT: Comparative Analysis of Bach Chorale Harmonizations

Five different harmonizations by Bach of a famous melody are given here. The melody is usually known as the "Passion Chorale" because Bach employed it no less than five times, in four different harmonizations, in his *Saint Matthew Passion* (1729); the melody itself was actually composed by Hans Leo Hassler as early as 1601. Bach's use of the melody is not confined to the grim context of Passion music; it also appears in his Cantatas Nos. 135, 153, and 161, and in the great *Christmas Oratorio*. The variety of uses of the melody accounts for the different texts associated with it, and, consequently, the different names by which it is called; the best-known German title is *Herzlich tut mich verlangen* (usually translated "My heart is filled with longing"), though *O Haupt voll Blut und Wunden* ("O sacred head, sore wounded") is also familiar.

In comparing the different versions given here, you should be attentive to initial progressions, first cadences, final cadences, the establishment of an apparent principal tonality, the appearance of a subsidiary or even a dual tonality, and the relationships between the more similar versions as well as the principal points of major difference.

The sources of the five versions are as follows:

Chorale No. 21, with text beginning "Und obgleich alle Teufel," from Cantata No. 153, *Schau', lieber Gott, wie meine Feind';*

Chorale No. 74, "O Haupt voll Blut und Wunden," is No. 77 of the *Saint Matthew Passion*, where it occurs just following the chorus "Hail, King of the Jews!" Here it has been transposed down a perfect fourth;

Chorale No. 80, "Befiehl du deine Wege," is No. 58 of the *Saint Matthew Passion*, following Pilate's questioning of Jesus. Here it is transposed down a major second;

Chorale No. 89, "Wenn ich einmal soll scheiden," is No. 93 of the *Saint Matthew Passion*, where it immediately follows Jesus's death;

Chorale No. 345, "Wie soll ich dich empfangen," is from Part I of the *Christmas Oratorio*.

If you wish to pursue this project even further, you should also examine Chorales Nos. 98, 286, and 367 (all of which somewhat resemble No. 80), and No. 270 (with flute obbligato), as well as the final chorus of Part VI of the *Christmas Oratorio*; in the latter version, the four-part harmonization, which is not found in the *371 Chorales*, has its phrases separated by brilliant ritornelli for three trumpets, timpani, two oboes, and strings.

Chorale No. 21

2.

3.

Chorale No. 80

4.

5.

The Sequence

SECTION A
Words to Know

Define and memorize:

harmonic sequence	regular sequence
tonal sequence	half sequence
initial pattern	interval of sequentiation
degree of transposition	

Contrast:

modulating sequence/nonmodulating sequence

Sections B (Technical Exercises) and D (Composition Activities) are not provided for this Unit.

SECTION C
Programmed Series

1. The following excerpt is preceded by harmony unambiguously in D major. This sequential passage serves as a codalike preparation for the final measures, also solidly in D major.

Schumann, *Papillons*, Op. 2, No. 12, Finale

In the blank staff provided below the excerpt, write a close-position chord indicating the harmony of each measure.

2. Are there one or more repeated patterns in the succession of roots of the chords you have written in No. 1 above? Explain here.

_____

_____

_____

3. Return to No. 1 and label all the chords. Copy the labels below as well, matching them to the appropriate measure numbers.

| 1 | 2 | 3 | 4 | 5 | 6 | 7 | 8 | 9 | 10 | 11 | 12 |

4. There is clearly a pattern between successive pairs of measures in the excerpt; the analysis you have just completed should also suggest to you that there is a larger pattern operating, in four-measure groups. Are the rhythmic, melodic, and harmonic elements in the excerpt all in a sequential pattern? Explain.

_____

_____

5. The interval between the first bass pitch of the initial pattern and that of the first transposition of the pattern is a _____ .

6. The interval between the first bass pitch of the first transposition and that of the second transposition is a _____ .

7. Compare the positions of the successive chords in the initial pattern with those of the chords in the subsequent transpositions.

_____

_____

_____

8. What are the successive intervals between the roots of the chords in the initial pattern?

_____

_____

_____

9. Are the intervals between the roots of the adjacent chords in the subsequent repetitions of the pattern in any way different from your answer to No. 8 above? _____

_____

_____

_____

_____

10. Considered in isolation, the initial pattern suggests the key of _____ .

11. The first transposition of the pattern, considered by itself, suggests the key of _____ . The last appearance of the pattern is of course in the principal key, D major.

12. The melodic, rhythmic, and harmonic ingredients of the initial pattern of the Schumann excerpt are literally repeated twice, each time a third higher. Does this constitute a "systematic transposition of a melodic, rhythmic, and harmonic pattern"?

_____

13. Considered in context, is the Schumann excerpt a nonmodulating or a modulating sequence? _____

14. Excerpts by Chopin, Beethoven, and Haydn follow. In locating the sequential patterns in these excerpts you should follow essentially the same procedures as in Nos. 1-13 above. Discuss your findings in the spaces provided below each excerpt, noting any variants in the repetitions that you may find, or anything else that adds to the individuality of a particular sequence.

Chopin, *Mazurka*, Op. 67, No. 2

(Compare the cycle-of-fourths sequence; see main text, pp. 257–58.)

Discussion:

Beethoven, *Sonata*, Op. 13 ("Pathétique"), III

Discussion:

Discussion:

SECTION E
Self Test

1. The harmonic sequence is defined as _____

_____

2. The pattern chosen for systematic transposition in the sequence is usually referred

to as the _____ .

3. A short phrase _____ be used as the pattern in a sequence.
  may well / is unlikely to

4. The harmonic rhythm usually _____ during subsequent repetitions
  changes / remains the same
of the pattern.

5. A single transposition of the pattern does not constitute a full sequence but rather

what might be called a _____ .

6. Usually a sequence will consist of the initial pattern and _____ repetitions.

7. A sequence that changes the tonal center with each transposition of the pattern is referred to as a _____ sequence.

8. Another name for the nonmodulating sequence is _____ sequence.

9. Secondary dominants _____ be included in a sequence.
   may / may not

10. Sequences _____ involve intermediate modulation.
    can also / never

11. A sequence may be used to modulate from one key to another. _____ (True or false)

12. In the commonest form of modulating sequence _____ keys are involved, and there _____ return to the principal key.
    is a / is no

13. In a modulating sequence the final chord of the pattern usually functions as the _____ .

14. A sequence in a melodic voice _____ accompanied by sequence
    is always / is not necessarily
    in the other voices, or in the harmony.

The Diminished Seventh Chord

SECTION A
Words and Symbols to Know

Define and memorize:

diminished seventh chord
dominant minor ninth chord
incomplete ninth chord
raised supertonic seventh chord
raised submediant seventh chord

V_9^0

$V_{\substack{6\\5}}^0$

$V_{\substack{4\\3}}^0$

$V_{\substack{4\\2}}^0$

SECTION B
Technical Exercises

1. The interval of a minor third is an essential component of the diminished seventh chord. Practice constructing minor thirds above and below each of the given tones.

2. The interval of the diminished seventh, or of its inversion the augmented second, is of course always present in the diminished seventh chord. To each of the tones given below, add a tone above so as to form a diminished seventh.

3. Your answers should look like what follows here. Make any necessary corrections, and then add a tone below each upper tone so as to form a minor third with it.

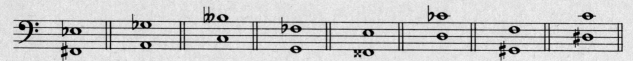

4. Answers to No. 3 are below. Add a minor third above the bottom note of each. The resulting four-note chord will consist of a minor third, a diminished fifth, and a diminished seventh interval from the bottom note to the top: a diminished seventh chord.

5. Check your answers to No. 4 with the chords given directly below. Now consider each chord to be the V_9^0 of a key, and name the key.

6. When the diminished seventh chord is in close position, with the leading-tone in the bass, it can be seen as a stack of minor thirds. Above each of the following tones, add a tone so as to form a minor third.

7. The minor thirds that you have just constructed should look like the following. Add another minor third above each of these to form a diminished triad.

8. If your diminished triads are correctly constructed they will be identical with these here:

Make any necessary corrections; then stack another minor third on top of each of the diminished triads, and diminished seventh chords will result.

190

9. The chords you have just constructed should in every respect resemble those given below. Label each of these according to the keynote to which it relates as V_9^0.

G: V_9^0

10. Write down the diminished seventh V_9^0 for each of the following keys. Write in the appropriate key signature and accidental signs.

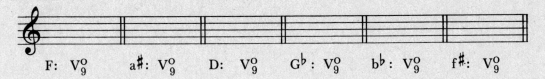

F: V_9^0 a♯: V_9^0 D: V_9^0 G♭: V_9^0 b♭: V_9^0 f♯: V_9^0

11. In the following, isolate the dissonant intervals. Label these intervals, label the chord itself, and indicate the key. Finally, write in the regular resolution of the diminished seventh chord.

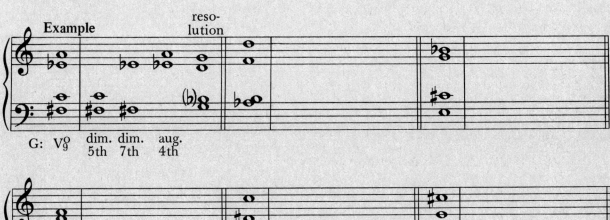

G: V_9^0 dim. dim. aug.
         5th 7th 4th

12. Construct secondary-dominant diminished seventh chords as indicated. Provide for each one a regular resolution, and label it.

f♯: V$^o_{6\atop5}$ of IV   d: V$^o_{4\atop3}$ of V   A♭: V$^o_9$ of II   E: V$^o_{4\atop2}$ of VI   B: V$^o_9$ of III

13. Label each chord below according to its function in relation to the key indicated. In addition, provide for each a regular resolution and label it.

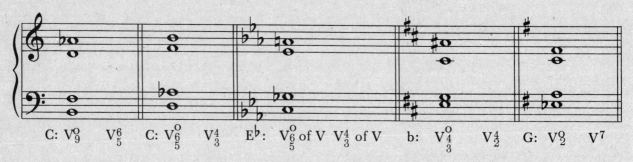

B♭:   f: A: E: C:

14. Resolve each of the given diminished seventh chords nonharmonically, as indicated by the figures.

C: V$^o_9$ V$^6_5$ C: V$^o_{6\atop5}$ V$^4_3$ E♭: V$^o_{6\atop5}$ of V   V$^4_3$ of V   b: V$^o_{4\atop3}$ V$^4_2$ G: V$^o_2$ V^7

15. Each chord given below is labeled, and the key is also indicated; the problem is that the chords are spelled incorrectly. As illustrated in the Example, renotate each chord, and then write and label its regular resolution.

Example

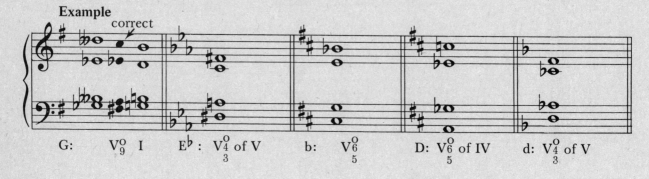

G: V$^o_9$ I   E♭: V$^o_{4\atop3}$ of V   b: V$^o_{6\atop5}$ D: V$^o_{6\atop5}$ of IV   d: V$^o_{4\atop3}$ of V

16. Work out the following derived figured bass.

Chopin, *Valse brillante*, Op. 34, No. 1 (adapted)

SECTION C

Analysis

This section contains a number of excerpts for analysis. Diminished seventh chords will be found here in contexts that are typical for their use. In analyzing the harmony of each excerpt, identify each diminished seventh chord, observe its relation to the principal key and to its chord of resolution, consider its relative duration and metric position, and take note of the voice-leading procedures that operate in relation to each chord.

The last three excerpts exhibit somewhat extended uses of the diminished seventh chord, and thus should be studied especially carefully. Block chords may be brought down into the blank staves below these excerpts, to facilitate analysis.

Additional space has been provided following each excerpt for discussion.

Beethoven, *Sonata*, Op. 13 ("Pathétique"), I

Discussion:

Schnell

Discussion:

Allegretto

Discussion:

Allegro vivace

Discussion:

Heil, dein Zit - tern und dein Za - gen ver - min - dern o - der hel - fen tra - gen, wie ger (ne)

Discussion:

Discussion:

Chopin, *Piano Concerto in E minor*, Op. II, III

Discussion:

197

Discussion:

Section D (Composition Activities) is not provided for this Unit.

SECTION E
Self Test

1. The diminished seventh chord may be thought of as a _____ chord, with its root omitted though implied.

2. In its closest position, with the leading-tone in the bass, the diminished seventh chord is a stack of _____ .

3. The diminished seventh chord includes the following dissonant intervals: two diminished _____ or augmented _____ , and one _____ seventh or augmented _____ .

4. The regular resolution of the V_9^0 diminished seventh chord is to the _____ triad, either major or minor.

5. What is generally a relatively infrequent doubling, but which results fairly often from the resolution of V_9^0 to I, is the doubling of the _____ of the tonic chord.

6. Secondary-dominant diminished seventh chords may relate to both _____ and _____ secondary tonics.

7. Why is the V_9^0 a useful pivot chord in modulation? _____
_____
_____
_____

The Incomplete Major Ninth

SECTION A

Words and Symbols to Know

Define and memorize:

half-diminished seventh chord
incomplete major ninth chord
VII ^{7}

Contrast:

half-diminished seventh chord/diminished seventh chord

SECTION B

Technical Exercises

1. Each of the following is either a diminished seventh chord or a half-diminished seventh chord. Circle all of the half-diminished seventh chords and indicate the key in which each is an incomplete dominant ninth.

2. Assuming the following half-diminished seventh chords to be incomplete dominants, identify the key involved in each case. Label each chord with suitable roman and arabic numerals, and write the appropriate regular resolution.

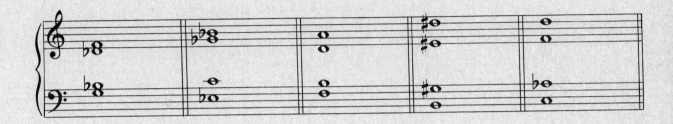

3. In the measures below, consider each given tone as a leading-tone. Build the half-diminished seventh chords as indicated, and name the key in which each will function as an incomplete major ninth.

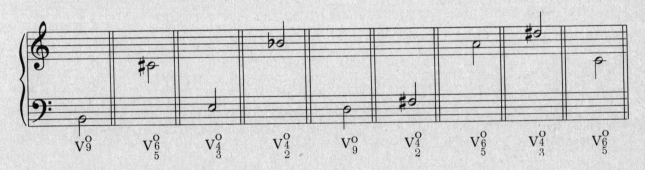

4. Identify the key in each of the following and provide the normal chord of resolution.

5. Construct the chords indicated and resolve each regularly.

G♭ : V⁰₉ of IV   A: V⁰₆₅ of IV   c: V⁰₉ of VI   g: V⁰₄₃ of V   C♯ : V⁰₆₅ of V

6. Each of the following derived figured basses contains an incomplete dominant ninth chord. Realize each bass in two versions, beginning each with a different spacing.

Wagner, Overture to *Tannhäuser* (adapted)

Mozart, *Sonata*, K. 284, III, Variation 5 (adapted)

Andante

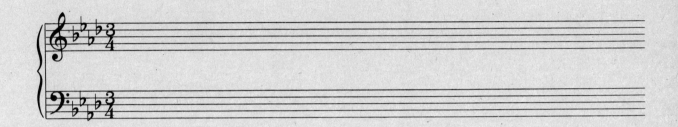

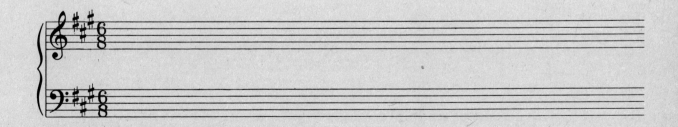

Analysis

Analyze the following excerpt, following the same guidelines specified in Section C of Unit Twenty.

Wagner, Prelude to *Die Meistersinger*

Discussion:

Section D (Composition Activities) is not provided for this Unit.

Self Test

1. The regular resolution of the major V_9^0 is to the _____ triad.

2. The half-diminished seventh chord may be obtained diatonically on the _____ degree of the major scale.

3. The essential structural difference between the diminished seventh chord and the half-diminished seventh chord is _____

_____

4. Unlike the diminished seventh, the half-diminished seventh shows a marked difference in the character of its _____ .

5. When is the designation VII^7 used in preference to V_9^0? _____

_____

6. A tendency throughout the period of harmonic common practice has been to treat the ninth in dominant harmony, whether or not the root is present, as a _____ tone, which is resolved to the tone below before the resolution of the chord takes place.

7. A half-diminished seventh chord in its third inversion will become a _____ when resolved nonharmonically.

8. Consecutive perfect fifths in the resolution of the half-diminished seventh chord are

_____ .
freely accepted / generally avoided

9. Doubling of the third in the tonic chord of resolution of the incomplete major ninth

is _____ .
usually practiced / usually avoided

10. The first inversion of the incomplete major dominant ninth is labeled _____ .

11. $V_{4\atop3}^0$ designates the _____ inversion of the half-diminished seventh chord.

12. The second inversion of the incomplete major ninth will normally resolve to either the _____ or _____ of the tonic chord.

13. The incomplete dominant major ninth _____ suitable for use in conjunction with the minor tonic.
is / is not

14. Irregular resolution of the incomplete major ninth occurs _____
somewhat frequently / relatively

_____ .
infrequently

15. Can all the degrees of the major mode be tonicized by secondary-dominant incomplete major ninth chords? _____ Explain why.

_____

_____

16. The most common secondary dominant incomplete major ninth chord is V_9^0 of

_____ .

17. The possibility of using the half-diminished seventh chord as a dominant pivot in modulation is _____ .
                                        fundamentally unlimited / somewhat restricted / nonexistent

The Complete Dominant Ninth

Words and Symbols to Know

Define and memorize:

$$V\;{}^{7}_{6}_{(5)}$$

dissolution
complete ninth
ninth effect

$$V\;{}^{6}_{5}_{4}$$

$$V^9$$

$$V\;{}^{4}_{3}_{2}$$

Technical Exercises

1. Write in close position the two complete ninth chords that are available in each of the following keys. Do not use key signatures, but write in the appropriate accidental signs directly.

Example

Bb   G   B   Gb   A

2. Construct each of the chords indicated in four parts. (The fifth will preferably be omitted.) In a few words, justify the spacing you have chosen in each case.

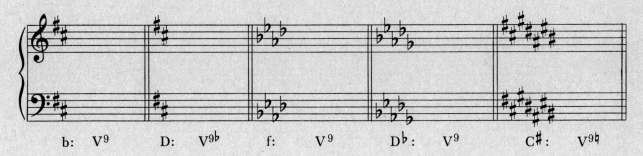

b: V^9 D: V^{9b} f: V^9 Db: V^9 C#: $V^{9\natural}$

Explanation:

3. Realize the following figured basses in four parts, in three separate versions of each according to the following different means of treating the ninth in dominant harmony:

a. Consider each ninth as a nonharmonic melodic tone, having special durational (agogic) or metrical stress, and resolving downward by step before the underlying harmony changes.

b. The ninth will be a chord tone that does not resolve by step, but disappears (dissolves) before the chord changes.

c. The ninth will be a chord factor, a harmonic dissonance that resolves down by step to a factor of the next chord.

Schubert, *Valses sentimentales*, Op. 50, No. 2 (adapted)

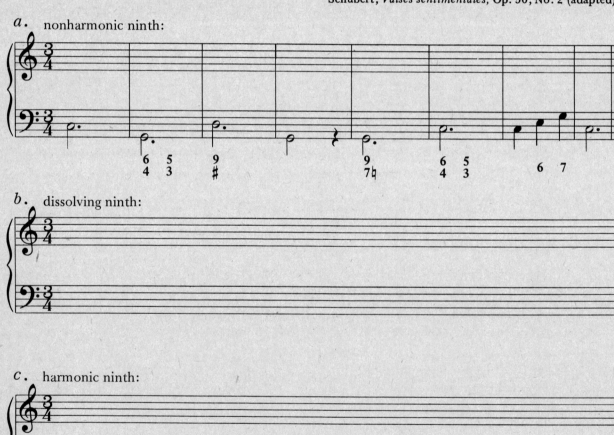

Allegretto

a. nonharmonic ninth:

b. dissolving ninth:

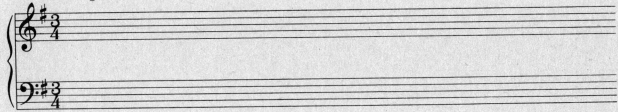

c. harmonic ninth:

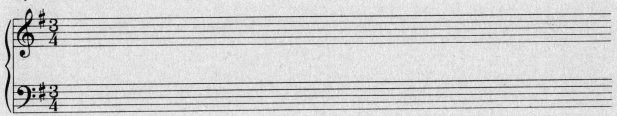

4. Work out only one version of the following modulating figured bass. Keep the appoggiature in the soprano voice.

Schubert, *Trauer-Walzer,* Op. 9, No. 2 (adapted)

Analysis

Analyze the following excerpts, labeling all chords and taking special note of the structure and function of the dominant ninth chords used.

Joplin, *The Entertainer*

Discussion:

Schubert, *Gretchen am Spinnrade*, Op. 2

Discussion:

Discussion:

Brahms, *Symphony No. 1*, II

Discussion:

Schumann, *Scenes from Childhood*, Op. 15: No. 4, *Pleading Child*

Discussion:

Section D (Composition Activities) is not included in this unit.

SECTION E
Self Test

1. When the complete dominant ninth is used in four-part writing, the chord factor most often omitted is the _____ .

2. The regular resolution of the complete dominant ninth is to _____ .

3. What are the three important aspects of the treatment of the ninth in dominant harmony by common-practice composers? _____

_____

_____

4. When the ninth is a nonharmonic tone, its usual resolution is by _____ in the _____ direction.

5. The resolution of the ninth into the chord that follows it is most usually by _____ , although on occasion it may be retained as a factor in the following chord.

6. Within a prevailing major mode, the ninth in dominant harmony will be _____

_____ .

   major / minor /
   either major or minor

7. Within a prevailing minor mode, the ninth in dominant harmony will be _____

_____ .

   major / minor /
   either major or minor

8. The form of the complete dominant ninth chord that was relatively infrequently used until the latter part of the nineteenth century is the _____ .

9. Discuss the usual spacing of the dominant ninth chord encountered in music of the common practice period. _____

_____

_____

10. How often is the complete dominant ninth found in one of its possible inversions?

_____ .

11. What inversion is not used, and why? _____

_____

12. Can the complete dominant ninth chord be used as a secondary dominant? _____

Nondominant Harmony–Seventh Chords

Words to Know

nondominant chords
dominant effect
major seventh chord
minor seventh chord
major-minor seventh chord

diminished seventh chord
half-diminished seventh chord
added-sixth chord
factitious root

SECTION B

Technical Exercises

1. Determine the characteristic structure of each of the seventh chords given below by listing the intervals that are formed between the root and each of the other chord factors. Give the name of the structural type of each chord (refer to page 349 of your main text).

Example

min. 3rd   perf. 5th   maj. 7th

major – minor seventh chord

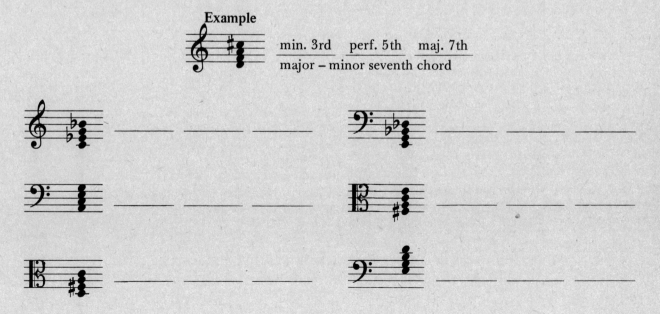

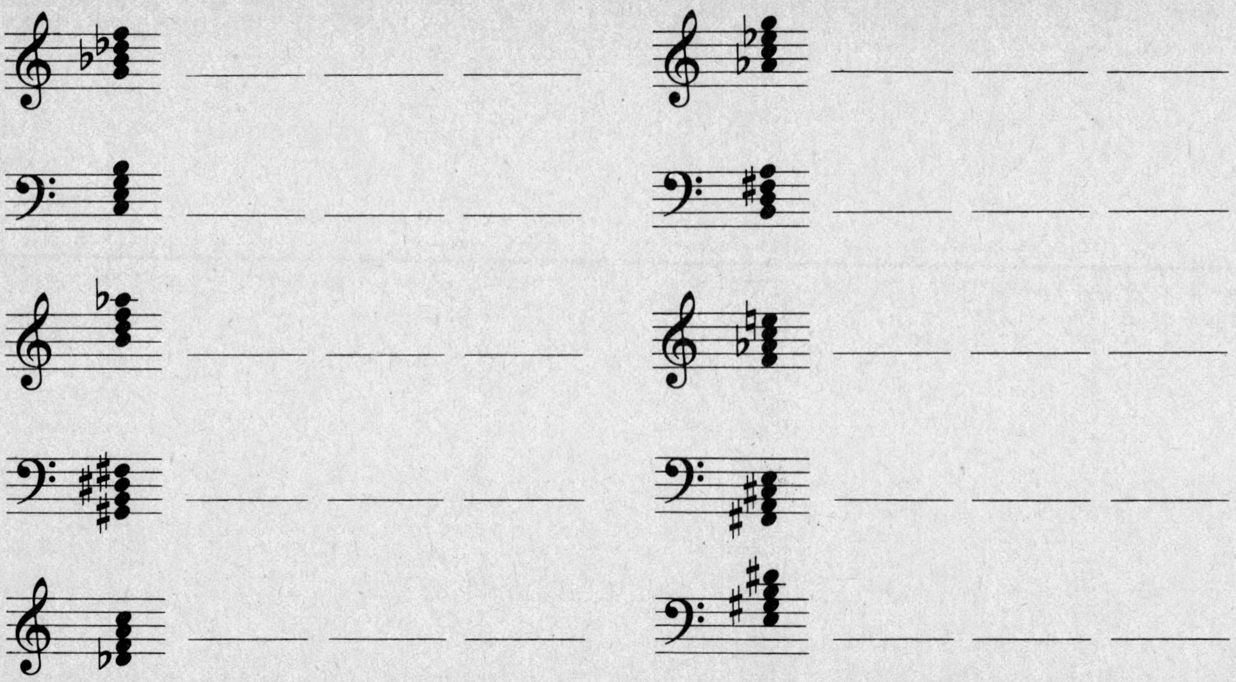

2. Below, write all of the diatonic seventh chords available in the key of A major.

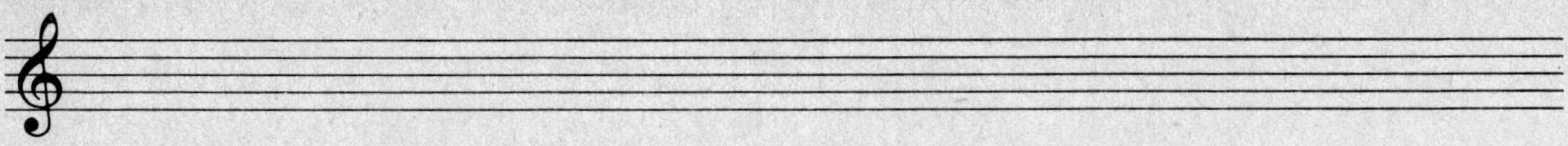

3. Referring to the chords you have just written in No. 2, consider each from the stand-point of structural type by listing below the intervals formed between the root and the other chord factors.

I^7: _____ , _____ , _____ II^7: _____ , _____ , _____

III^7: _____ , _____ , _____ IV^7: _____ , _____ , _____

V^7: _____ , _____ , _____ VI^7: _____ , _____ , _____

VII^7: _____ , _____ , _____

4. Now list together in groups the symbols of those seventh chords of the major scale that are of the same structural type, and give the names of the types.

_____ : _____

_____ : _____

_____ : _____

_____ : _____

5. Below, write all of the diatonic seventh chords available using the notes of any one harmonic minor scale. (Use a key of your choice.)

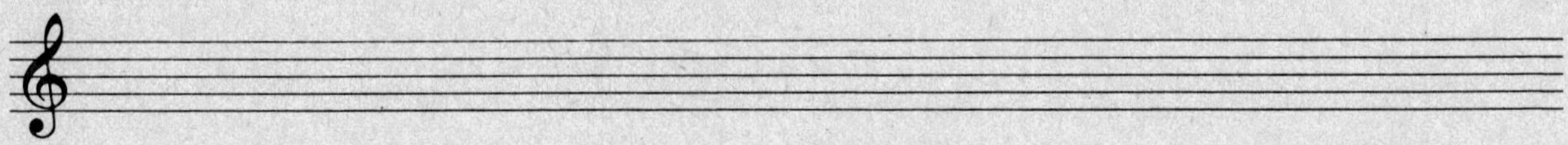

214

6. Referring to the chords you have just written in No. 5, consider each from the standpoint of structural type by listing the intervals formed between the root and the other chord factors.

I⁷: _____ , _____ , _____   II⁷: _____ , _____ , _____

III⁷: _____ , _____ , _____   IV⁷: _____ , _____ , _____

V⁷: _____ , _____ , _____   VI⁷: _____ , _____ , _____

VII⁷: _____ , _____ , _____

7. Now list together in groups the symbols of those seventh chords of the harmonic minor scale that are of the same structural type, and give the names of the types.

_____ : _____

_____ : _____

_____ : _____

_____ : _____

8. Construct the diatonic seventh chords and their resolutions as indicated below.

B♭ : I⁷   I   F♯: I⁷   IV   f: I⁷   IV⁷   E: I⁷   II⁶₅   c: II⁶₅   V   G: II⁶₅   I⁶₄   V

A♭: III⁴₃   VI⁶   A: IV⁷   IV(II)⁶₅   IV⁷ V   c♯: IV⁷   V⁴₃   I   a: IV⁷   II⁶₅   V   E♭: IV⁴₂   II⁷   V

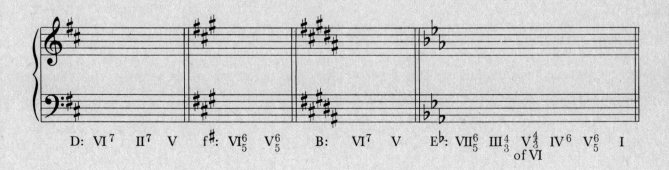

D: VI⁷   II⁷   V   f♯: VI⁶₅   V⁶₅   B: VI⁷   V   E♭: VII⁶₅   III⁴₃   V⁴₃   IV⁶   V⁶₅   I
                                                                                    of VI

9. Work out two versions, differing in spacing and general texture, of each of the following figured basses.

Grieg, *Voegtersang* (adapted)

Molto andante

Mozart, *Rondo*, K. 494 (adapted)

Grazioso e giocoso

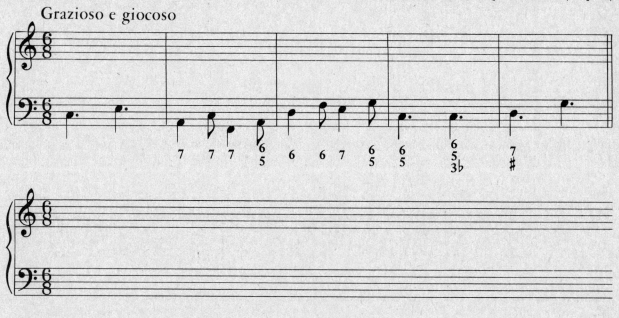

SECTION C
Analysis

Analyze the following excerpts, paying particular attention to the use of nondominant seventh chords. Discuss your findings in the space provided.

Schumann, *Dichterliebe*, Op. 48: No. 7, *Ich grolle nicht*

Discussion:

Bach, *Fugue in E-flat major for organ* ("St. Anne")

Discussion:

Composition Activities

Write a short piece approximately sixteen measures long in moderate tempo for a melody instrument with piano accompaniment. Make use of II^7 and one of its inversions at various points in the piece, especially during the course of a modulation wherein II^7 (or its inversion) in the initial key serves as a pivot chord (VI^7) in the second key. When the new key is established, come to a cadence with the progression IV^7–II^6_5–I^6_4–V^7–I. Conclude your piece in the new key, or, if you wish, modulate back to the original key. Be certain to indicate tempo, articulation, dynamics, and phrasing.

Self Test

1. The strongest characteristic of dominant harmony is the presence of the

    _____ , a _____ above the root of the dominant chord.

2. The structural type of the different seventh chords is determined by _____

    _____

3. The intervallic structure of a dominant seventh chord is _____ , _____ , and _____ above the root.

4. How many different structural types of nondominant diatonic seventh chords are

    there in common use? _____

    _____

5. The major seventh chord consists of a _____ , a _____ , and a _____ above the root.

6. The minor seventh chord is composed of a _____ , a _____ , and a _____ above the root.

7. A minor third, diminished fifth, and minor seventh above a given root constitute a

    _____ seventh chord.

8. The major-minor seventh chord contains the intervals of _____ , _____ , and

    _____ above a given root.

9. The customary resolution of the seventh in a nondominant seventh chord is by

    _____ in a _____ direction.

10. The _____ seventh occurs fairly often as an upward-resolving appoggiatura to the octave of the root.

11. Harmonically, the regular resolution of a nondominant seventh chord is to the chord whose root is a _____ higher.

12. When the fifth of a nondominant seventh chord is omitted, the _____ is usually doubled.

13. Generally the nondominant seventh chords _____ be used in any in-version.
    may freely / may not

14. The tonic seventh chord regularly resolves to _____ .

15. The commonest resolution of the supertonic seventh chord is to the _____ chord.

16. The subdominant seventh chord resolves usually either to _____ or to _____ , which in turn regularly resolves to the dominant.

17. The leading-tone seventh chord in the major mode, usually an incomplete major dominant ninth, partakes of nondominant characteristics when it proceeds to _____ .

18. The supertonic seventh chord in first inversion can in many instances be regarded more convincingly as a _____ triad with added sixth.

19. The added sixth in tonic or subdominant harmony is a type of _____ disso-nance analogous to the seventh in dominant-seventh harmony.

20. The added sixth in subdominant and tonic harmony does not usually have the strength of a true root and therefore is called a _____ root.

21. The use of a major tonic triad with added sixth and with vanishing fifth became a nationalist mannerism in the works of many nineteenth-century _____ com-posers.

Ninth, Eleventh, and Thirteenth Chords

SECTION A
Words to Know

Define and memorize:

appoggiatura with delayed resolution
unresolved appoggiatura
eleventh chord
thirteenth chord

SECTION B
Technical Exercises

Resolve the following ninth chords, treating the ninth appropriately to the specifications given.

a. Appoggiatura:

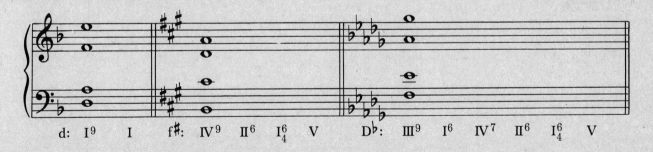

$$\text{d: } I^9 \quad I \qquad \text{f\#: } IV^9 \quad II^6 \quad I^6_4 \quad V \qquad \text{D\flat: } III^9 \quad I^6 \quad IV^7 \quad II^6 \quad I^6_4 \quad V$$

b. Appoggiatura with delayed resolution:

$$\text{C: } IV^9 \quad V^7 \quad III^9 \quad IV^7 \qquad \text{E\flat: } II^9 \quad VII^7 \quad I^9 \quad VI^7$$

c. Appoggiatura unresolved:

A♭: V⁹ V⁹ of IV   E: IV⁹ II⁶₅   C: II⁹ V¹³ V⁷

Analysis

The following excerpts are offered for detailed analysis, with particular attention to ninth, eleventh, and thirteenth chords.

Bach, *Three-Part Invention No. 5*

Discussion:

222

Discussion:

Bizet, *l'Arlésienne Suite No. 1*: No. 3, *Adagietto*

Discussion:

Discussion:

The final excerpt given here is lengthy, but its full extent is necessary to show the developmental process in all its completeness. (Compare the melody given in Chapter 7 of your main text, page 106, Exercise 1*c*.)

Bruckner, *Symphony No. 7*, I

Discussion:

Section D (Composition Activities) is not provided for this unit.

Self Test

1. The nondominant ninth chord effects used by composers in the period of common-practice harmony are generally found on the roots _____ , _____ , and _____ .

2. The appoggiatura to the octave above the root in the bass is a potential source of the effect of a _____ chord.

3. Pedals, appoggiature, and suspensions are often used so as to bring about the effect of _____ and _____ chords.

4. The resolution of the appoggiatura or suspension may be _____ until after the harmony changes.

5. A dominant seventh chord superposed above a tonic pedal will create the effect of a _____ .

6. What is commonly referred to as the _____ is often created by the subdominant triad sounding above a dominant pedal.

7. The dominant eleventh may result from the combination of dominant pedal with a _____ seventh.

8. Thirteenth chords may be found resulting from superposing a dominant ninth above a _____ pedal.

9. The commonest form of dominant thirteenth is an upper appoggiatura to the _____ of the dominant triad; the _____ is usually included also, but the _____ or the _____ , or both, may be missing.

Chromatically Altered Chords: The Raised Supertonic and Submediant

---

Words and Symbols to Know

Define and memorize:

chromatically altered chord	tendency tone
+II	appoggiatura chord
+VI	auxiliary chord

Technical Exercises

1. Construct the following raised II and VI chords and their resolutions, as indicated.

$A\flat : +II^7 \quad I^6 \qquad C: +VI^2 \quad V^7 \qquad G: +II^6_5 \quad I^6_4 \qquad C\flat: +VI^4_3 \quad V^2 \qquad B\flat: +II^4_3 \quad I^6_4$

$A: +II^2 \quad I \qquad B: +VI^6_5 \quad V^4_3 \qquad D\flat: +II^7 \quad I^6 \qquad C\sharp: +VI^7 \quad V^6_5 \qquad F\sharp: +II^6_5 \quad I^6_4$

227

F: $^+VI^4_3$ V^2 G♭: $^+II^4_3$ I^6_4 E: $^+II^2$ I   D: $^+VI^6_5$ I^4_3 ·E♭: $^+II^7$ $I6$

2. Realize each of the following figured basses in four parts. Label all keys and chords. Below each exercise, briefly discuss the particular use of the chords being studied in this unit.

Schumann, *Twelve Pieces for Piano Four Hands for Children Big and Small*, Op. 85: No. 12, *Evening Song*

Ausdrucksvoll und sehr gehalten

Discussion:

Bizet, *Carmen*, Act II (adapted)

Allegretto moderato

Discussion:

Discussion:

Sections C (Programmed Series) and D (Composition Activities) are absent from this unit.

SECTION E

Self Test

1. Give five reasons why accidental signs, indicating chromatic alterations of scale degrees, will arise in music:

   a) _____

   b) _____

   c) _____

   d) _____

   e) _____

2. In the key of D major, nondominant diminished seventh chords may be constructed on the notes _____ and _____ .

3. The $^{+}II^{7}$ in the key of G major is spelled _____ , _____ , _____ , _____ .

4. A$^{\times}$, C$^{\times}$, E♯, G♯ is the spelling for the $^{+}VI^{7}$ in the key of _____ .

5. The normal resolution of $^{+}VI^{7}$ is to the _____ chord of the prevailing major key.

6. In the major mode, $^{+}II^{7}$ is ordinarily followed by _____ .

7. A plus sign (+) placed at the upper left of a roman numeral indicates that

_____ .

8. The ^{+}II and ^{+}VI _____ be found in strong metrical positions.
will occasionally / will never

9. The raised supertonic and submediant chords are more at home in the _____ mode than they are in the _____ .

10. The raised supertonic and submediant seventh chords _____
can be used very effectively / are of little
_____ in modulation.
practical use

230

The Neapolitan Sixth

SECTION A

Words and Symbols to Know

Define and memorize:

Neapolitan sixth chord N^6
lowered supertonic $^-II^6$

SECTION B

Technical Exercises

1. Spell the Neapolitan triad in the following keys:

Example:

C major	D♭	F	A♭		C-sharp minor	____	____	____
F major	____	____	____		D minor	____	____	____
G major	____	____	____		D-flat major	____	____	____
E major	____	____	____		A-flat major	____	____	____
A minor	____	____	____		G minor	____	____	____

2. Complete each of the following in four parts, taking care to observe proper doubling and voice leading with respect to the Neapolitan sixth chord. Then write a second version of these progressions, using a different spacing for the initial chord, and different keys of your choice.

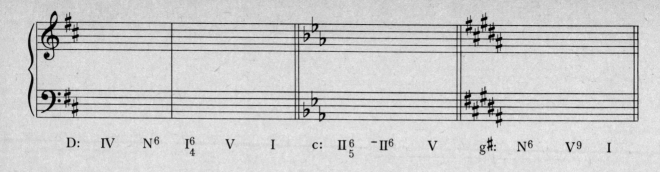

D: IV   N⁶   I⁶₄   V   I   c: II⁶₅   ⁻II⁶   V   g♯: N⁶   V⁹   I

3. Work out the following figured basses; then briefly discuss the uses of the Neapolitan chords in each.

Mendelssohn, *Song without Words*, Op. 102: No. 4, *The Sighing Wind* (adapted)

Un poco agitato, ma andante

Discussion:

Etwas langsam

Discussion:

SECTION C

Analysis

Analyze and discuss the use of Neapolitan harmony in the following excerpt.

Franck, *Prelude, Chorale, and Fugue*

Poco allegro

Discussion:

Section D (Composition Activities) is omitted in this unit.

Self Test

1. The Neapolitan sixth chord is a _____ triad whose root is the _____ degree of the prevailing scale.

2. The Neapolitan sixth chord _____ used in the first inversion.
   is always / is not necessarily

3. The symbol ⁻II signifies _____ .

4. The Neapolitan sixth is a _____ chord.
   consonant / dissonant

5. The Neapolitan sixth ordinarily progresses to some form of _____ harmony.

6. The tone that is usually doubled in the Neapolitan sixth is the _____ because it is a _____ degree in the scale.

7. The root of the Neapolitan generally moves to the _____ by the interval of a _____ .

8. Very often the Neapolitan will move through a _____ before moving to the dominant chord.

9. The use of the Neapolitan sixth chord is limited to cadential formulae. (True or false?) _____

10. The Neapolitan sixth _____ a useful pivot chord in modulation.
    is / is not

11. The special value of the Neapolitan sixth in modulation is _____

    _____ .

Augmented Sixth Chords

SECTION A

Words, Symbols, and Abbreviations to Know

Define and memorize:

augmented sixth chord	$^{+}\text{II}{}^{6+}_{4+}$
augmented six-five-three	3
augmented six-four-three	It.
doubly augmented fourth	Ger.
lowered fifth	Fr.

Contrast:

French sixth/German sixth   French sixth/German sixth
German sixth/doubly augmented fourth   doubly augmented fourth/raised supertonic seventh

SECTION B

Technical Exercises

1. Add tones above those given below so as to form augmented sixth intervals.

2. The answers to No. 1 are given directly below. To these, add a major third above each lower tone.

3. Now you have the three factors which are constant in every augmented sixth chord, regardless of type. Adding the proper fourth factor will specify the type. Above the bass of each chord, write in the tone specified by the interval given below, and name the chord that results.

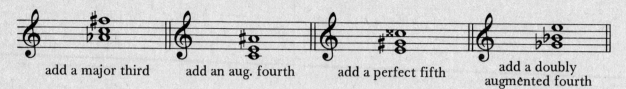

add a major third   add an aug. fourth   add a perfect fifth   add a doubly augmented fourth

4. Your answers should look like the following. Make any necessary corrections, and then indicate the key in which each of these augmented sixth chords belongs.

Italian   French   German   doubly augmented fourth (chord without a country)

5. Construct the augmented sixth chords indicated and their resolutions.

236

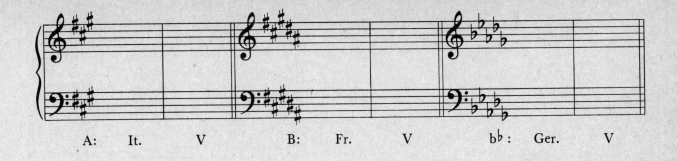

A: It.   V   B: Fr.   V   bb: Ger.   V

SECTION C

Analysis

Analyze the following excerpts, all of which contain augmented sixth chords. Discuss the structure, type, and function of these chords and how they relate generally to the context.

Schubert, *Winterreise*, Op. 89: No. 10, *Rast*

mit heis - sem Stich sich re - gen,   fühlst in— der— Still' erst—

dei - nen Wurm   mit heis - sem Stich sich re - gen!

Discussion:

Discussion:

Discussion:

Discussion:

Discussion:

This unit contains no Section D (Composition Activities).

Self Test

1. In any augmented sixth chord, regardless of structural type, the tonic pitch will always be present, as well as the _____ degree, and the _____ degree.

2. The resolution of the augmented sixth interval is nearly always to the _____ on the _____ .

3. In addition to the tonic, raised fourth, and minor sixth degrees, the Italian sixth has _____ .

4. The type of augmented sixth chord whose minor sixth degree forms the interval of augmented fourth with one of the factors is the _____ .

5. Another name for the augmented six-five-three is _____ .

6. The doubly augmented fourth chord resolves regularly to _____ .

7. The regular resolution of the Italian, German, and French sixths is to _____ .

8. Two of the augmented sixth chords are enharmonically equivalent to a dominant seventh chord and thus are useful in deceptive modulations; these two chords are the _____ and _____ .

9. The inverted augmented sixth chord, in which the interval of diminished third is formed between the bass and one of the upper parts, is of relatively _____
   occurrence.   frequent / rare

10. The augmented sixth chords are _____ used in modulation.
                                     often / seldom

Other Chromatic Chords

SECTION A
Words and Symbols to Know

augmented fifth chord   omnibus progression
diminished fifth chord V^{5+}
appoggiatura chord V^{5-} etc.

SECTION B
Technical Exercises

Work out the following progressions in four parts (five, in one case).

Sections C (Programmed Series) and D (Composition Activities) do not appear in this unit.

SECTION E

Self Test

1. Triads with fifth raised to make the interval of augmented fifth with the root are found on _____ , _____ , and _____ .

2. The altered tone usually _____ doubled.

is / is not

3. The tonic chord with raised fifth resolves regularly to _____ .

4. The dominant seventh chord _____ appear with a raised fifth or a lowered fifth.

may / may not

5. The dominant with raised fifth implies the _____ mode.

6. The usual chord to follow a dominant with raised fifth is the _____ .

7. The expected chord of resolution for the subdominant with raised fifth is the

   _____ .

8. The dominant with lowered fifth will ordinarily be followed by _____ .

9. The dominant triad with its fifth simultaneously raised and lowered normally proceeds to _____ .

10. The omnibus progression is essentially a V_5^6–II_4^6–V^7 with chromatic _____ in between.

11. The diverging chromatic progression from I^6 to II^7 (major mode) with _____ in between was a favorite progression of the latter part of the nineteenth century.

12. Many chromatically altered chords that can be written will not sound in the way that their notation implies, because they will be heard _____ as simpler structures.

Answers to Self Tests

UNIT ONE: Scales and Intervals

1. octave
2. seven
3. five
4. whole, whole, half, whole, whole, whole, half
5. tonic
6. tonic, supertonic, mediant, subdominant, dominant submediant, and leading-tone
7. intervals
8. lines and spaces, *or* letter names, *or* scale degrees
9. major
10. melodic
11. harmonic
12. major, minor, augmented, diminished
13. perfect, augmented, diminished
14. compound
15. simple
16. consonant
17. dissonant
18. perfect unison, perfect octave, perfect fifth, major third, minor third, major sixth, minor sixth, and (sometimes) perfect fourth
19. dissonant
20. dissonant
21. minor
22. diminished
23. perfect
24. second
25. minor sixth
26. enharmonic equivalents
27. F, C, G, D, A, E, and B
28. B, E, A, D, G, C, and F
29. G, D, A, E, B, F sharp, and C sharp
30. F, B flat, E flat, A flat, D flat, G flat, and C flat

UNIT TWO: Triads

1. chord
2. triad
3. thirds
4. root; third; fifth
5. inverted
6. fifth
7. first
8. minor; augmented; diminished
9. major third; perfect
10. diminished
11. major third; augmented
12. They are alike in that they both have a perfect fifth; they are different in that the major triad has a major third between root and third, while the minor triad has a minor third.
13. major; minor
14. augmented; diminished
15. I; IV; V
16. minor
17. diminished
18. is not
19. soprano; alto; tenor; bass
20. doubling
21. root
22. is not
23. larger; smaller

UNIT THREE: Triads

1. root
2. frequently
3. strong
4. weak
5. common
6. connected
7. "If the two triads [to be connected] have one or more notes in common, these are usually repeated in the same voice, the remaining voice or voices moving to the nearest available position." (Text, p. 34)
8. II–V (when the fourth degree of the scale is the soprano of the II chord)
9. "If the two triads have no tones in com- opposite direction to the bass, always to the nearest available position." (Text, p. 25)
10. V–VI
11. fifth; double
12. third; fifth
13. No
14. The interval of augmented fourth, or its inversional or enharmonic equivalent the diminished fifth, is called the tritone because it is the sum of three whole-tone steps.
15. "When two voices move upward in similar motion, the lower voice is not usually allowed to move to a position higher than that just left by the upper voice . . . . The corresponding rule holds for descending movement." (Text, p. 33)

UNIT FOUR: The Minor Mode

1. F, G, A$^\flat$, B$^\flat$, C, D$^\flat$, E$^\flat$
2. relative major
3. minor; below
4. minor; above
5. True
6. seventh
7. seventh; major
8. third; sixth; lower
9. sixth; seventh; raised
10. no different
11. third
12. harmonic
13. infrequently
14. essentially the same as

UNIT FIVE: Tonality and Modality

1. tonality
2. key; scale
3. Dorian; Phrygian; Lydian; Mixolydian
4. may
5. tonic (or keynote)
6. dominant; subdominant
7. I, II, IV, and V
8. C and F
9. III and VI
10. authentic cadence
11. musical words
12. does not
13. Their scales are made up of the same notes, and they have the same key signature.
14. the Picardy third
15. tonicized
16. parallel
17. chromatic

UNIT SIX: The First Inversion—The Figured Bass

1. third
2. 6
3. roman; arabic
4. I^6
5. second
6. that the tones a sixth and a third above the bass, or their compounds, are to be sounded
7. the position of the doubled degree in the scale
8. is not
9. is
10. C
11. are no
12. dominant
13. dominant
14. most often
15. VI
16. leading-tone
17. tonic
18. third; fifth; root
19. figured bass
20. that the tone indicated by the numeral is to be chromatically raised
21. that the third (or its compound) above the bass is to receive the sign indicated
22. that the note indicated by the figure will be maiptained in the harmony until the end of the line, even if the bass changes

UNIT SEVEN: Function and Structure of Melody

1. melody
2. countermelody
3. thirds or sixths
4. ostinato
5. figuration
6. motive
7. phrase
8. antecedent and consequent
9. Ornamentation

UNIT EIGHT: Nonharmonic Tones

1. nonharmonic
2. Yes
3. True
4. conjunct
5. consonance
6. resolve
7. stepwise
8. opposite
9. weak
10. appoggiatura
11. anticipation
12. passing tone
13. rhythmically weak
14. "a tone whose natural progression has been rhythmically delayed." (Text, p. 122)
15. appoggiatura
16. escape tone
17. reaching tone
18. escape tone and reaching tone

UNIT NINE: The Harmonic Structure of the Phrase

1. four or eight
2. fewer
3. long
4. downbeat; upbeat
5. cadence; cadence
6. half; authentic
7. masculine; feminine
8. sequence
9. rhythm

UNIT ELEVEN: The Six-four Chord

1. second
2. fifth
3. perfect fourth
4. an unstable
5. fifth
6. cadential
7. a) it is rhythmically strong with respect to its resolution; b) its fifth is doubled; and c) the other two voices resolve downward by step, like appoggiature.
8. downward by step
9. is
10. noncadential (or noncadential appoggiatura)
11. may
12. a) it is rhythmically weak; b) the bass is like a passing tone between two tones belonging to the same harmony; and c) one of the upper voices is like a neighbor note while another upper voice is like a passing tone moving in opposite direction to the bass.
13. auxiliary
14. weak
15. tonal; modal
16. a) it is rhythmically weak; b) the bass is stationary with respect to the preceding and following chords; and c) two of the upper voices move as neighbor notes.
17. bass
18. I–V$^6_4$–I^6 or the reverse; IV–I$^6_4$–IV^6 or the reverse

UNIT TWELVE: Cadences

1. cadences
2. V to I
3. II or IV
4. may
5. strong
6. perfect
7. imperfect; final
8. half
9. IV to I
10. is occasionally
11. deceptive
12. submediant
13. Phrygian

UNIT THIRTEEN: Harmonic Rhythm

1. root; rhythmic
2. No
3. should
4. nonharmonic
5. need not
6. strength
7. static
8. restlessness
9. static

UNIT FOURTEEN: Modulation

1. static
2. form
3. three
4. is not
5. pivot chord
6. four
7. four (allowing for modal interchange)
8. enharmonic
9. dominant
10. dominant
11. does not constitute
12. time
13. intermediate
14. True
15. modulation chain
16. related
17. are
18. are
19. practically identical
20. minor; major
21. would
22. abrupt
23. shift

UNIT FIFTEEN: The Dominant Seventh Chord

1. major; perfect; minor
2. II and VII; VII; III
3. minor seventh; diminished fifth
4. major second; augmented fourth
5. consonant
6. major third or minor third
7. descend stepwise
8. upward by step to the tonic
9. downward by skip to the dominant
10. major sixth or minor sixth
11. tonic
12. roots; third
13. usually
14. fifth
15. upward to the dominant
16. four-two
17. is
18. I^6
19. four-three; six-four

UNIT SEVENTEEN: Irregular Resolutions

1. tonic triad
2. VI
3. regular
4. incomplete
5. They have the same root, and therefore the same quality of root motion.
6. weak
7. not at all
8. VI
9. deceptive
10. step
11. a perfect fourth; a perfect fifth
12. stepwise upward
13. VI
14. I; up; tonic

UNIT NINETEEN: The Sequence

1. the systematic transposition of a melodic, harmonic, and rhythmic pattern
2. initial pattern
3. may well
4. remains the same
5. half sequence
6. two
7. modulating
8. regular
9. may
10. can also
11. True
12. three
13. pivot chord
14. is not necessarily

UNIT TWENTY: The Diminished Seventh Chord

1. dominant minor ninth
2. minor thirds
3. fifths; fourths; diminished; second
4. tonic
5. third
6. major and minor
7. The diminished seventh chord is useful as a pivot chord in modulation because it may be interpreted enharmonically as a dominant in any of four different keys, as a secondary dominant in several more, and as a nondominant chromatically altered chord in others still.

UNIT TWENTY-ONE: The Incomplete Major Ninth

1. major tonic
2. seventh
3. that the interval between the root and the seventh is a major seventh rather than a minor seventh, meaning that the chord is not the result of superposition of equal intervals
4. inversions
5. when the dominant effect of the chord has been weakened, for instance before III
6. melodic
7. dominant seventh chord in root position
8. generally avoided
9. usually practiced
10. $V^{0}_{6{}_5}$
11. second
12. root position or first inversion
13. is not
14. relatively infrequently
15. No, because minor triads cannot serve as secondary tonics for the incomplete major ninth.
16. V
17. somewhat restricted

UNIT TWENTY-TWO: The Complete Dominant Ninth

1. fifth
2. I
3. a) as a nonharmonic tone; b) as a harmonic dissonance resolved through arpeggiation (dissolution) before the harmony changes; and c) as a harmonic dissonance resolving to a tone of the following chord
4. step; downward
5. step downward
6. either major or minor
7. minor
8. major
9. The most usual spacing is root position with the ninth a ninth (or an octave plus a ninth) above the root, with the leading-tone above the root but below the ninth.
10. Not often
11. The fourth inversion is not used because the ninth would then be below the root.
12. Yes

UNIT TWENTY-THREE: Nondominant Harmony—Seventh Chords

1. leading-tone; major third
2. the intervals between the root and the other factors
3. major third, perfect fifth, and minor seventh
4. Seven
5. major third, perfect fifth, and major seventh
6. minor third, perfect fifth, and minor seventh
7. half-diminished
8. minor third, perfect fifth, and major seventh
9. step; downward
10. major
11. perfect fourth
12. root
13. may freely
14. IV
15. V
16. VII, or to II^7
17. III
18. subdominant
19. harmonic
20. factitious
21. Russian

UNIT TWENTY-FOUR: Ninth, Eleventh, and Thirteenth Chords

1. I, II, and IV
2. ninth
3. eleventh and thirteenth
4. delayed
5. tonic eleventh chord
6. dominant eleventh
7. supertonic
8. tonic
9. fifth; seventh; ninth; eleventh

UNIT TWENTY-FIVE: Chromatically Altered Chords: The Raised Supertonic and Submediant

1. a) inflections of the sixth and seventh degrees in the minor mode; b) chromatic nonharmonic tones, such as passing tones and neighbor notes; c) inflections in secondary dominants; d) modulations without the key signature being changed; and e) chromatically altered chords
2. E♯ and B♯
3. A♯, C♯, E, and G
4. C♯ major
5. dominant six-five
6. I^6
7. the root is raised
8. will occasionally
9. major; minor
10. can be used very effectively

UNIT TWENTY-SIX: The Neapolitan Sixth

1. major; lowered second (lowered supertonic)
2. is not necessarily
3. that the root is lowered
4. consonant
5. dominant
6. third; tonal
7. leading-tone; diminished third
8. tonic six-four
9. False
10. is
11. its common ground between distantly related keys

UNIT TWENTY-SEVEN: Augmented Sixth Chords

1. raised fourth; minor sixth
2. octave on the dominant
3. a second tonic pitch
4. French
5. German
6. I$^6_4$
7. V
8. German sixth and doubly augmented fourth
9. rare
10. often

UNIT TWENTY-EIGHT: Other Chromatic Chords

1. I, IV, and V
2. is not
3. IV
4. may
5. major
6. tonic triad
7. II^6
8. I
9. I
10. passing chords
11. I^6 (minor) with simultaneous raised and lowered fifth
12. enharmonically

Writing for Instruments– Some Elementary Information

This Workbook is based on the assumption that most of you play the piano only, and that you have not studied orchestration or instrumental methods. Yet often in your Composition Activities you are asked to write for instruments that may be unfamiliar to you. In writing for those instruments that your fellow students play, you will be able to learn much from what they can tell you and demonstrate for you. This appendix is provided to get you started on the right track, so you do not write impractical or impossible notes.

Some of the problems in learning to write for instruments are purely mechanical and will disappear with familiarity and practice. Probably the biggest initial difficulty is in transposition, which must be mastered since approximately a third of the orchestral instruments, and more than half of the band instruments, sound pitches different from the notes they read and play. Transposition of instruments is discussed separately in Appendix III.

Other problems are conceptual, and will require you to learn what is instrumentally practical, to put yourself in the player's mind, as it were. For instance, it is not difficult to learn that the flute is a monophonic instrument and cannot play complete chords the way a piano can; but it is also essential to remember that the flute and all other wind instruments are lung-powered rather than hand-powered, and therefore require rests so that the player can breathe. (As a general rule, the bigger the wind instrument, the more breath will be needed.) Another conceptual problem has to do with qualities of articulation, which differ widely among instruments, yet are part of their very nature; for instance, a slur placed over a succession of notes means a particular kind of articulation for a flute, another for a trombone, still another for a violin; the familiar long slurs stretching over several measures in a piece of piano music are seldom used in writing for winds or strings.

Finally, there is the question of instrumental sound, which is tantamount to saying: "Will it work?" This does not mean "Can it be played?" nearly as much as "Will it sound good?" As you learn to solve the mechanical and conceptual problems, you will come to see that the problems of instrumental sound, whether for single instruments or combined instruments, are the most interesting and challenging of all. It is not for this Workbook to begin to meet such challenges, other than to say that your work on the Composition Activities, and the practical realization of them by actually having them tried out repeatedly, will be excellent preparation for further study in instrumentation. Those of you who become serious composers or orchestrators will always be aware that actually hearing your music will reveal more than any amount of systematic study.

One should begin by learning the practical extremes of range of the most familiar instruments. The ranges given here are those considered accessible by average-to-good players; the given notes and all those in between are playable. More advanced students will be able to play somewhat higher, and in the case of most brass instruments somewhat lower as well. For most of the woodwinds, the highest notes are difficult to make sound well; for the brasses, difficult notes at either end of the range are either strident or weak. The tone quality of well-played strings is excellent over nearly the entire range.

It is important to remember that the ranges above include the notes that the instruments can actually *sound.* Instruments marked with a T in parentheses are transposing instruments, which are not notated as they sound (see Appendix III); all others sound as they are written.

Sounding ranges

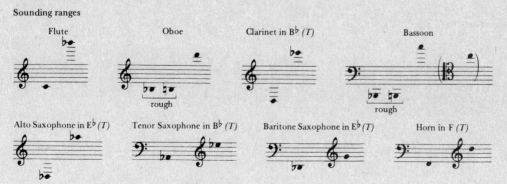

Some instruments use more than one clef through their range. The bassoon, trombone, and cello all employ the tenor clef (middle C on the fourth line of the staff) freely in the high register, or, less often, the treble clef. The viola uses the alto clef (middle C on the third line) nearly all the time; most violists would rather read several ledger lines above the alto clef than change to the treble clef for moderately high notes. As a rule, the *8va* sign used everywhere in keyboard music is not congenial to wind and string players, because of fingering differences. A pattern fingered in a certain way on the piano will be fingered identically an octave higher; this is by no means the case in winds and strings. Orchestra players are used to reading *8va*, but generally they find it more comfortable to read extra ledger lines unless these are clearly impractical.

For further reading on this subject, Walter Piston's *Orchestration* (W. W. Norton, 1955) is recommended.

APPENDIX III

Transposing Instruments

The following summary lists only the transposing instruments likely to be encountered in a college music environment. In your study of scores you will from time to time encounter less familiar instruments requiring transposition, such as the *violino piccolo* of Bach's *Brandenburg Concerto No. 1*, or the horns in F sharp in Haydn's *Symphony No. 45*. The various treatises on orchestration will tell you about a good many of these; but if you master the transpositions of the standard instruments listed here, you will be able to figure out nearly any other kind of transposing instrument on your own.

The following charts and tables all represent different ways of stating the same kinds of relationships. Choose those that suit you best.

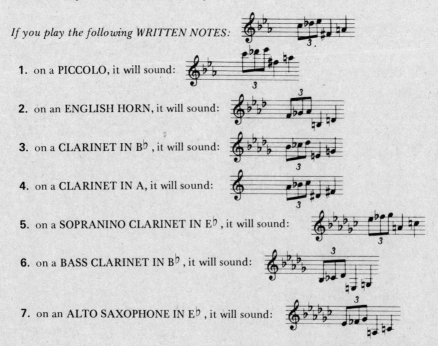

If you play the following WRITTEN NOTES:

1. on a PICCOLO, it will sound:

2. on an ENGLISH HORN, it will sound:

3. on a CLARINET IN B♭ , it will sound:

4. on a CLARINET IN A, it will sound:

5. on a SOPRANINO CLARINET IN E♭ , it will sound:

6. on a BASS CLARINET IN B♭ , it will sound:

7. on an ALTO SAXOPHONE IN E♭ , it will sound:

8. on a TENOR SAXOPHONE IN B♭ , it will sound: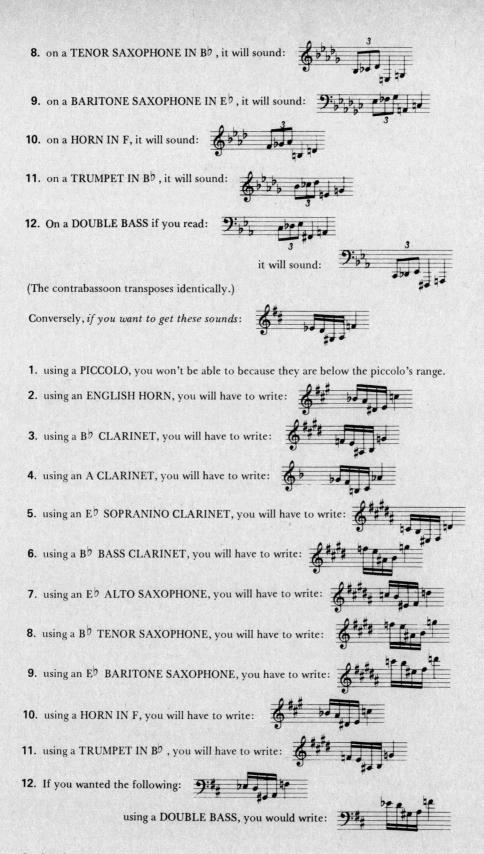

9. on a BARITONE SAXOPHONE IN E♭ , it will sound:

10. on a HORN IN F, it will sound:

11. on a TRUMPET IN B♭ , it will sound:

12. On a DOUBLE BASS if you read:

it will sound:

(The contrabassoon transposes identically.)

Conversely, *if you want to get these sounds*:

1. using a PICCOLO, you won't be able to because they are below the piccolo's range.

2. using an ENGLISH HORN, you will have to write:

3. using a B♭ CLARINET, you will have to write:

4. using an A CLARINET, you will have to write:

5. using an E♭ SOPRANINO CLARINET, you will have to write:

6. using a B♭ BASS CLARINET, you will have to write:

7. using an E♭ ALTO SAXOPHONE, you will have to write:

8. using a B♭ TENOR SAXOPHONE, you will have to write:

9. using an E♭ BARITONE SAXOPHONE, you have to write:

10. using a HORN IN F, you will have to write:

11. using a TRUMPET IN B♭ , you will have to write:

12. If you wanted the following:

using a DOUBLE BASS, you would write:

Stating these rules in words instead of examples:

1. The piccolo sounds one octave above the written notes.

2. The English horn sounds a perfect fifth below the written notes.

3. The B♭ clarinet sounds a major second below the written notes.

4. The A clarinet sounds a minor third below the written notes.

5. The E♭ sopranino clarinet sounds a minor third above the written notes.

6. The B♭ bass clarinet sounds an octave and a major second below the written notes (an octave below the ordinary B♭ clarinet).

7. The E♭ alto saxophone sounds a major sixth below the written notes.

8. The B♭ tenor saxophone sounds an octave and a major second below the written notes (i.e., just like the bass clarinet).

9. The E♭ baritone saxophone sounds an octave and a major sixth below the written notes (an octave below the alto saxophone).

10. The horn in F sounds a perfect fifth below the written notes (i.e., just like the English horn).

11. The trumpet in B♭ sounds a major second below the written notes (just like the ordinary B♭ clarinet).

12. The double bass sounds a perfect octave below the written notes (so does the contrabassoon).

Or, to put it another way:

1. Write the part for the piccolo one octave lower than you want it to sound.

2. Write the part for English horn a perfect fifth higher than you want it to sound.

3. Write the part for B♭ clarinet a major second higher than you want it to sound.

4. Write the part for A clarinet a minor third higher than you want it to sound.

5. Write the part for E♭ sopranino clarinet a minor third lower than you want it to sound.

6. Write the part for B♭ bass clarinet an octave and a major second higher than you want it to sound.

7. Write the part for E♭ alto saxophone a major sixth higher than you want it to sound.

8. Write the part for B♭ tenor saxophone an octave and a major second higher than you want it to sound.

9. Write the part for E♭ baritone saxophone an octave and a major sixth higher than you want it to sound.

10. Write the part for horn in F a perfect fifth higher than you want it to sound.

11. Write the part for trumpet in B♭ a major second higher than you want it to sound.

12. Write the part for double bass an octave higher than you want it to sound.

As you become familiar with these transpositions you will get an idea of how the key signatures are changed by them and how accidental signs are affected. The rule given in Chapter 18 of your main text is worth repeating here: in a part for an instrument "in X," the written note C sounds X.